A Guide to the
CARRIAGE OF DANGEROUS GOODS

including full list of

Names of dangerous substances

Identification numbers

Emergency action codes

Primary hazards created by various substances

by
W.J. DOBSON

HEADLIGHT PUBLICATIONS LTD
52-54 Southwark Street, London SE1 1UJ

ISBN 1 870093 01 1

Copyright 1987 by William J. Dobson

Printed in Great Britain by Mayhew McCrimmon Printers Ltd, Great Wakering, Essex and typeset by JJ Typographics, Cottis House, Rochford, Essex.

INTRODUCTION

THE 'Dangerous Goods Handbook' is intended to be a useful reference document, which can be conveniently carried in an overall pocket. It is for both experienced drivers and those new to chemical, petroleum product and hazardous waste transportation. It is produced in sections.

Section 1 is a general introduction to dangerous goods and subject matter common to all types of conveyance.

Section 2 includes an easy-to-follow explanation of current tanker/tank container regulations which clearly identify the driver as having direct responsibility for ensuring the vehicle is correctly marked, is parked in accordance with specific criteria and many other similar rules. Failure to honour these obligations can result in breaches of the regulations answerable in a criminal court. This section also includes some general procedures that constitute good habits or safe working practices for bulk loads.

Section 3 is similar in content to Section 2 but is written specifically for drivers who transport dangerous substances in packages, drums, carboys, cylinders, sacks, etc. The general haulage driver will find himself having to understand and comply with new regulations that place additional responsibility on him.

Section 4 contains a list of most prescribed dangerous substances, the classification of each, product identification and packing group numbers. It is necessary to have this information available before vehicles are loaded.

It has become clear to me through my employment with a large well known tanker operator and also from my contact with some 5,000 drivers attending the national approved tanker driver safety course, Hazfreight, that a convenient size handbook would be well received by them. I am indebted to them for their ideas and comments expressed while the handbook was in its formative stages. They are all sensible enough to know that the written word cannot cover all variations of circumstances so it is with a word of warning that I close this introduction.

Good habits and safe procedures are the underlying basis for ensuring that unusual occurrences are quickly identified and are coped with before there is danger to the driver or others in the vicinity. Never take anything for granted or take short cuts. Remember that if you wish to be seen and treated as a professional there is no room in the haulage industry for those who cannot meet the standards reasonably expected by the general public of a professional.

So, when in doubt, think and obtain advice from a suitable source before you act.

W. J. Dobson

SECTION 1

**Dangerous substances: Chemicals, Petroleum Products
and Hazardous Wastes.**

THE words "dangerous substance" mean little or nothing to
the great majority of people. Yet when a dangerous substance
is spilled on our roads or is the cause of a factory fire, great
publicity is given to it. However, these dangerous substances
play a major part in improving the lives of us all. The use of
chemicals has greatly increased the output of our farms. In
medicine, the use of chemicals has increased our life expectancy.
In the home, chemicals have made our lives more comfortable.

In a society where the use of dangerous substances is
widespread, it is essential that laws are passed to protect us all.
Inevitably, the transportation and storage of these products
comes within the scope of these laws. Dangerous substances
have to be clearly marked as such. The main way this is done is
with a symbol either in the form of a diamond or square. The
diamonds are frequently seen on road tankers and drums.

The square shapes are usually found on small packages,
often in shops. You will see them on bottles of bleach or tins of
paint.

In addition to these shapes which will carry warning symbols
like a fire, other risks are also identified. The bottle or tin may
carry such phrases as:—

> May cause fire, or
> Harmful if swallowed.

Other safety phrases may tell you how safely to store the
product:—

> Keep container in a well-ventilated place
> Avoid contact with skin.

There are many such phrases. Hazards can be classified
according to properties or effect. The main ones are:—

> Flammable
> Corrosive
> Gases
> Poisonous/Toxic Substances
> Other Hazards — Solvents

Flammable means it can be set on fire. A liquid does not
burn, so first it has to give off vapours or gases which when
mixed with air can be set on fire. Most flammable vapours are

heavier than the surrounding air so they tend to collect in pockets in areas like cellars or under the stairs. Therefore, never use flammable products below ground level without forced ventilation.

Corrosive substances are chemicals which destroy flesh and clothing, in particular. So special clothing is required when working with them. Eye protection is a must, together with plastic gloves and an apron.

Many gases are converted into a liquid form to make usage and storage more convenient. Butane and propane used for cooking are actually boiling inside their containers. It is this which creates the pressure to feed your cooker. These containers must be kept cool, particularly if a fire breaks out. Otherwise they will become over-pressurised and explode.

Poison/toxics are injurious to health when you come into contact with only very small quantities. The body can be affected either by inhalation (breathing in the vapours), absorption (soaking in) or ingestion (swallowing).

There are two other product groups represented by the symbol "X" which means they are not considered to be as dangerous as the corrosives or toxics. So two other words are used to describe them — irritant or harmful. Many of the herbicides, pesticides, fungicides and biocides fall into these categories. It should be stressed that many of these subjects marked as harmful are also volatile. This means they readily give off vapours which if inhaled can lead to dizziness or even unconsciousness.

To sum up, here are some simple rules for using chemicals and petroleum-based products:—

1. Read the label and understand the properties and hazards of the product.
2. Use protective clothing, paying particular attention to the eyes.
3. Work safely, being aware of possible trapped vapours and other people working in the area.

The three golden rules for storage are:—

1. Make sure the place is cool so that liquids do not expand and leak.
2. Make sure the place is dry so that labels do not get damp and fall off and so that tins do not rust.
3. Make sure the place is secure so that children cannot get at the products.

One final warning: If you have any doubts, do nothing till you can get advice.

Common Terminology

SOME words in common use when dangerous substances are being conveyed are found on the Tremcard (Transport Emergency Card). It is important for drivers and other persons involved with transporting chemicals and petroleum products to understand words such as:—

Absorption	Soaking in, such as water into your clothes or into the ground.
Ambient	Surrounding, such as the ambient temperature being the temperature outside.
Aqueous	Containing water, for example water being a constituent part of a soft drink or perhaps contained in a solid.
Corrosive	Destructive, such as acid burning into a metal.
Decomposes	Breaks down chemically, a typical example being a garden compost heap.
Evaporate	Changes from liquid to vapour.
Flammable/ Inflammable	Burns easily.
Flashpoint	A volatile product (see below) readily evaporates and the vapour produced can be ignited at its flashpoint temperature.
Immiscible	Does not mix with other chemicals, for example oil is immiscible with water.
Inert	Non-reactive. Inert usually refers to gas and means it does not react or explode.
Inhalation	Action of breathing in. Clearly, some gases or vapours should not be inhaled.
Miscible	The opposite of immiscible (above), meaning will mix with other chemicals.
Narcotic	A substance which causes unconsciousness, perhaps deliberately in medicine but often by accidentally breathing in dangerous fumes.

Notionally Empty/	
Nominally Empty	Empty, but uncleaned. This term is used in connection with road tankers and also for drums/carboys, etc. which contain small quantities of residual product or vapours.
Oxidising Agent	A chemical which supplies oxygen and therefore aids burning. This product group also increases oxidisation as with the case of oxygen in water causing rust.
Perceptible Odour	Noticeable smell.
Toxic	Poisonous to touch, inhale or ingest, such as arsenic.
Ullage	The space above the liquid in a container into which expansion can take place should there be a rise in temperature and pressure.
Viscous	A viscous liquid is one that is thick and flows slowly.
Volatile	A volatile substance is easily and quickly changed from liquid to vapour.

The Tremcard

TREMCARD is a shortened version of the words Transport Emergency Card. It is used to provide the emergency services with essential information in the event of an accident, product spillage or similar occurrence.

An appropriate Tremcard (or equivalent) is to be carried for each prescribed dangerous substance conveyed on the road in a road tanker, tank container, flat vehicle, van or other type of vehicle in scope to either current tanker or package/drum conveyance regulations.

All Tremcards are written in the same format so that the relevant information appears in the same place on each card and it is deliberately designed that way to ensure that a fire or police officer attending the scene of an accident can quickly assess the degree of risk involved at any incident.

Standard Tremcard layout is as follows:—

1. Cargo	The product name and any alternative name(s) and a brief description of its properties.
2. Nature of hazard	What problems can arise if the product is not handled correctly.
3. Protective devices	Protective equipment and devices required for dealing with an emergency such as spillage. The scale of equipment suggested is not necessarily the same as the driver's protective equipment.
4. Emergency action	This section lists immediate action to be taken in an emergency but the exact sequence of events will be determined by the circumstances and could include keeping the public away from the scene, preventing sources of ignition being used in the vicinity, etc. Always notify the emergency services immediately.
5. Spillage	Action to be taken and advice on how to minimise risk when clearing up spillage.
6. Fire	How to tackle a product fire and advice on correct type of extinguisher.
7. First aid	What first aid treatment may be necessary if persons are affected by the product.
8. Additional information	Can include advice or recommendations which may be helpful when dealing with an emergency.
9. Telephone number	A specialist advice telephone number should be stated.

Tremcard(s) for the load should be clearly displayed in the cab of the vehicle on a clipboard or similar holder. All other tremcards should be removed from the vehicle or placed in a receptacle marked "Not in Use".

For a typical Tremcord see inside back cover.

SECTION 2

The Dangerous Substances (Conveyance by Road in Road Tankers and Tank Containers) Regulations 1981 (effective from 1 January 1982).

THE regulations are supported by the following supplementary documents available from HMSO: (a) Approved Code of Practice (b) Guidance Note (c) Approved list of Dangerous Substances. The significant point to make about the Code of Practice is that while it is not legislation itself, it is admissible as evidence in court and may well serve as proof of failure to comply with the regulations.

What is a dangerous substance?
- Those substances shown in the approved list.
- Substances not named in the approved list but having the same characteristic properties as those that are listed.

What is conveyance?
- In the case of a road tanker, from the start of loading for the purpose of conveying the substance on a road until the tank or compartment of the tank has been cleaned or purged risk free.
- In the case of a vehicle carrying a tank container, from either

    1. The time at which a loaded tank container is placed on the vehicle, or
    2. If the container was empty, from the time loading starts for the purpose of conveying the substance by road until either,
    3. The tank container is removed from the vehicle, or
    4. The tank container, or compartment of the tank container, has been cleaned or purged risk free, and, in either case, whether or not the vehicle is on a road.

Who is the vehicle operator?
- In the case of a road tanker, the person who holds, or is required to hold, an operator's licence under section 60 of the Transport Act 1968.
- Where no such licence is required, the keeper of the vehicle.
- In the case of a tank container, the owner of the tank container or his agent, if that person has a place of business in Great Britain, and
- Is identified as the owner or his agent by markings on the

tank container itself or on the documentation carried in the vehicle.

If no person satisfies the above criteria, the operator of the vehicle on which the tank container is carried.

A person to whom a tank container is leased or hired shall, in law, be deemed to be the owner.

When do the regulations apply?

- To all road tankers irrespective of size.
- To all tank containers which have a capacity of 3 cubic metres, 3,000 litres if 660 gallons.
- When carrying a dangerous substance as defined above when conveyance is in progress.

When do regulations not apply?

- To substances not defined as dangerous e.g. sand, starch, glucose, sugar, gas oil, derv, etc.
- To vehicles travelling to and from U.K. ports on international journeys providing the relevant international rules are being fully complied with, for instance:—

  ADR — the European Agreement on international carriage of dangerous goods

- To vehicles under the control of the armed forces.
- To vehicles exempt from excise duty.
- To certain road construction vehicles.

Vehicle construction

The vehicle operator is responsible for ensuring any vehicle or tank container conveying dangerous substances by road:—

- Is properly designed, of adequate strength and of good construction.
- Is suitable in all respects for the purpose for which it is being used.
- Is adequately equipped with the correct ancillary equipment such as flexes, hoses, flanges, fittings, etc.
- Has been periodically tested and retested after modification, accident damage, etc.
- Has a tank certificate in existence for that particular vessel which indicates the substances it may convey.

Information in writing

The vehicle operator is responsible for:—

- Providing (or arranging for someone else to provide) the driver with a Tremcard (or equivalent) before loading starts.
- Providing somewhere, e.g. a clipboard, for the driver to display a Tremcard in a prominent position in the cab.

- Providing a secure and clearly marked container for the driver to store Tremcards (or equivalent) not in use.

The driver is responsible for:—

- Displaying the Tremcard (or equivalent) in the cab while conveyance is taking place.
- Placing spare Tremcards (or equivalent) in the "not in use" container.
- Transferring Tremcard (or equivalent) to filled or nominally empty trailers left solo when away from base.
- Ensuring a transferred Tremcard is protected from weather.

Precautions against fire and explosion

All persons, including the operator, driver, terminal staff, mechanics working on the vehicle while loaded, vehicle examiners, police officers, customs officers, etc. having contact with a vehicle when conveying dangerous substances have a responsibility to take all precautions necessary to prevent fire and explosion when any of the following products are conveyed:—

> flammable liquids or gases
> liquid oxygen, organic peroxides or other strongly oxidising substances
> spontaneously combustible substances
> substances which are dangerous when wet.

The driver is responsible for:—

- Checking that the vehicle carries not less than one serviceable 1 kg dry powder or BCF extinguisher in the cab and one 9 kg dry powder or 20 litres foam on the vehicle (protected from the weather).
- Not smoking during loading or unloading and during conveyance when there is a possibility of flammable gas or vapour being present in the cab.
- Preventing others in the close vicinity from smoking.
- Removing potential sources of ignition from the vehicle when it is being loaded or unloaded (cigarette lighters, non-sparkproof torches and radios, etc.).
- Ensuring that master switches, earthing leads, etc., are serviceable and used.
- Stopping loading/unloading if there is a fire or thunder in the vicinity.
- Not starting the vehicle engine until all connections have been made.
- Stopping the vehicle engine before any connection is broken.
- Being alert to dangers arising from electrical faults, binding brakes, low tyre pressures, overheating engines, etc.

- Not using portable cookers in the cab.

Overfilling

The operator is responsible for:—

- Ensuring sufficient ullage is allowed.
- Informing the driver, if responsibility is delegated to him/her, what is the maximum permitted quantity of product to be loaded into any particular tank.

The driver is responsible for:—

- Ensuring that the load is correctly distributed to avoid axle overweight.
- Ensuring the load does not present a danger or nuisance to other road users.

Supervision and parking of vehicles

Tanks bearing an "E" in the Hazchem board coding, those displaying substance identification numbers 1268 containing toluene or petroleum distillate with flashpoint below 21°C or 1270 containing petrol, are subject to specific parking and supervision rules, except when nominally empty. These tanks must be:—

- Constantly supervised by the driver or by another trained person over the age of 18 years, or be
- Parked in a safe place.

Safe places are:—

- A park specifically approved for dangerous loads.
- A place in the open air to which the public does not have access e.g. a factory or a transport depot.

If neither of these alternatives can be arranged:—

- A place not on a road or lay-by where the public do not usually pass or gather and not less than 15 metres from occupied premises.
- A disused loop road.
- A motorway service area in a place where the public does not usually pass or gather and not less than 15 metres from occupied premises.
- Certain places of accommodation provided the park is private property away from the road and the vehicle is not within 15 metres of occupied premises.
- Vehicles with different hazard warning diamonds should, where practicable, not be parked near each other unless one or both of them is nominally empty. They should be so parked that they can be moved in an emergency.
- The motive unit should not be detached from its trailer when it is parked as above.

Parking for less than one hour

- Vehicles should be parked within sight (as far as is reasonably practicable) and within easy reach.
- If this is not possible another trained driver should be asked to fulfill these two requirements.
- If it is necessary to call a breakdown service or make a 999 call the driver should stay with his vehicle and get someone else to make the call.
- In the event of a breakdown the tractor should remain coupled to the trailer until a replacement arrives.

Security during parking

Except when the vehicle is parked in secure premises the load must be made safe against theft and interference.

Instruction and training for drivers

The operator is responsible:—

- For ensuring the driver receives adequate instruction and training in:

> The hazards of dangerous substances that his duties will require him to convey.
> Loading and unloading procedures.
> Use of safety equipment.
> Emergency procedures.
> Checks before starting journeys.
> Vehicle marking.
> Tremcards (or equivalent).
> Knowledge of relevant legislation.

- For keeping a record of training attended by a driver and making it available to the driver should he change his employment.
- For giving the driver adequate instructions on the particular load he is to convey.
- For periodic, or additional, training as necessary to comply with regulations.

Operators are free to use their discretion as to how they arrange driver training but the general standard required is that compatible with the national training scheme organised by the co-sponsors of the Hazfreight Course. They are:

> The Chemical Industries Association.
> The Road Haulage Association.
> The National Association of Waste Disposal Contractors.
> The Petroleum Training Federation.
> The Road Transport Industry Training Board.

14

Tanker Marking

This is fully explained under the "Tanker Marking" section but, briefly, drivers' responsibilities are summarised as follows:

Hazard warning panels must be:—

- Displayed on both sides and at the rear of tankers.
- Displayed midway on both sides of tank containers.
- Weather resistant and indelibly marked on one side only.
- Securely attached and at least one metre from the ground with side panels on tankers as close as possible to the front of the tank.
- Kept clean and free from obstruction.
- Remain on display until the tank is cleaned or purged or removed from the vehicle.

Compartment labels must be:—

- Displayed on multi-loads midway on both sides of compartments.
- Weather resistant, securely attached and marked on one side only.
- Kept clean and free from obstruction.

Panels and labels on tanks which have been cleaned or purged must be:—

- Completely removed or covered.
- Partly covered or removed so as to leave visible only the specialist advice telephone number.

Delivery of petroleum spirit

Special rules apply and these are explained in the "Delivery of petroleum spirit" section.

Loading and unloading

All drivers of tankers or tank containers are required to be competent vehicle operators. Additionally they have a responsibility to:—

- Familiarise themselves with written terminal procedures.
- Stop loading or unloading when necessary, such as an unexpected incident occurring.
- Take steps to ensure that his/her vehicle does not move accidentally.
- Not enter a road tank without authorisation to do so.
- Ensure that he/she does not load petrol on a multi-load vehicle along with other substances.

Enforcement

Enforcement responsibilities for these regulations rest with the police and the Health and Safety Executive.

Daily Checks and Normal Procedures.

THE nature of a driver's work is such that because they are often away from their home depot for long periods and are without direct supervision, it is necessary for them to use initiative and resourcefulness to ensure a delivery is completed. The checks listed below are suggested as general guidelines for drivers engaged in transporting dangerous substances in tanks, but, given the variety of the work, they can only form the basis of good habits. They cannot cover all variations and circumstances.

Daily checks on the vehicle
Check levels and/or suitability on the following:—
- Oil.
- Coolant.
- Lights.
- Tyres.
- Foot valve.
- Outlet valve.
- Blanking caps.
- Fire extinguisher(s)
- Manlids and seals.
- Hoses and flexes.
- Flex fittings and blanking caps.
- Pump and compressor.
- Earthing points.
- Ladders.
- Catwalks.
- General visual inspection.

Before loading checks
- Identify product and quantity to be loaded from consignment or delivery note.
- Ensure Tremcard (or equivalent) is available.
- Ensure hazard warning panels are available.
- Ensure protective equipment, as detailed on Tremcard, is available and can be taken with the driver whilst conveyance takes place.
- Ensure tank is certificated as being suitable for the product to be conveyed.
- Ensure tank fittings are correct type for load i.e. stainless steel, mild steel etc.
- Ensure tank barrel has sufficient capacity for load and is clean.

At the loading point
- Report to the Supervisor.
- Obey local safety rules.
- Obtain instructions for berthing the vehicle.
- Ascertain whether loading will be carried out by plant operative alone or whether the driver is to remain in attendance.
- Make all necessary connections.
- Wear safety equipment as detailed on Tremcard (or equivalent).
- Earth vehicle.
- Fit hazard warning panels.
- Display Tremcard (or equivalent) in cab.

After loading and before departure checks
- Ensure correct quantity has been loaded and the vehicle is not overweight.
- Complete a visual inspection of vehicle to ensure it is roadworthy.
- Ensure all manlids and valves are securely closed.
- Ensure clean and legible hazard warning panels are fitted at appropriate points on tank — always three in number on tankers and two on tank containers.
- Ensure only the Tremcard (or equivalent) is displayed in cab and *all* "not-in-use" Tremcards are placed in a secure container.
- Ensure flexes, fittings and other loose equipment is secured.
- Ensure there are no leaks from valves, lid seals, etc.
- Ensure earthing lead is disconnected.

At the discharge point
- Report to the Supervisor.
- Obtain instructions regarding storage vessel into which load is to be discharged and how it can be identified.
- Berth vehicle correctly.
- Wear safety equipment detailed on Tremcard.
- Earth vehicle.
- After ensuring discharge flexes are correct type, connect up, including vent connection if necessary — do not start engine until all flexes are connected and always switch off engine before disconnecting flexes when discharging by pump or compressor.
- If using flange joints, check bolts and gasket.
- Confirm customer ready for the load.
- Open valves and commence discharge.
- Check for leaks.

- Stay in attendance throughout.
- When discharge complete, close storage tank inlet valve after closing tank barrel valves and draining hoses.
- Disconnect discharge flexes and earth lead.
- Check flexes and other loose equipment stowed.
- Obtain signature for load.
- Carry out visual inspection of vehicle, to ensure it is in a condition fit for travel.

The tank is now in a condition known as "nominally" or "notionally" empty but is in scope to conveyance regulations because of the small quantity of residual product and fumes still in the barrel. Consequently hazard warning panels are still displayed and the Tremcard (or equivalent) carried in the cab. This will continue to be the case until the tank is cleaned or purged and is deemed to be risk free.

Tanker Marking

Single product

Tanker and tank container vehicles conveying dangerous substances in scope to the U.K. domestic legislation i.e. The Dangerous Substances (Conveyance by Road in Road Tankers and Tank Containers) Regulations 1981, are required to display hazard warning panels. Hazard warning panels are sometimes referred to as Hazchem boards. A conventional road tanker is required to display three warning panels from the time that loading starts to the time when the tank barrel has been cleaned or purged and is risk free. These panels must be fitted as follows:—

- One on each side of the tank as near the front as is practical.
- One on the rear of the tank in a position where it is clearly visible.

  For tank containers, as soon as a loaded ISO tank becomes part of the vehicle, then marking requirements apply as follows:—

- One warning panel is to be displayed midway on both sides of the tank.

  For both conventional tankers and tank containers the driver is responsible for:—

- Displaying hazard warning panels as required.
- Ensuring they are securely attached at least one metre above the ground.
- Ensuring they are weather-resistant and indelibly marked on one side only.

- Ensuring they are kept clean and free from obstruction.
- Ensuring they remain on display until the tank is cleaned or purged or removed from the vehicle.

The format of Hazard Warning Panels is laid down in the regulations and it is as shown below:—

Emergency Action Code — | — Hazard Diamond

Substance Identification Number —

— Company logo (optional)

Emergency telephone number

The information to be displayed for Emergency Action Code, Substance Identification Number and Hazard Classification Diamond are listed against each product in Section 4 of this book.

Multi-loads

Road tankers conveying more than one product are said to be carrying a multi-load. The same rules apply as detailed above but the hazard warning panel must display the words "MULTI-LOAD" instead of a Substance Identification Number. Each compartment of the tank must bear a compartment label on both sides displaying the Substance Identification Number.

Tank containers carrying more than one product also must display one multi-load hazard warning panel on each side, mounted in a central position, plus a compartment label on both sides displaying the Substance Identification Number.

COMPARTMENT LABEL

Low-hazard loads

While there is no legal obligation to do so, many operators comply with a recommendation made by the Chemical Industries Association to display black-and-white low hazard warning panels on road tankers conveying products such as derv and gas oil. These petroleum based products are not defined as dangerous substances because they have a flash point greater than 55 degrees Centigrade. However, there is a small risk so the emergency services should be warned accordingly. Tremcards are also available for low hazard products. A typical black-and-white hazard warning panel is as shown below:—

It is recommended that all road tankers and tank containers carry an indication of products being carried. When a tank contains prescribed dangerous substances there is no choice. But for low risk products use of the voluntary black-and-white scheme is helpful to emergency service personnel.

Emergency action codes

The Emergency Action Code to be displayed on a road tanker or tank container is laid down in the regulations. It is strictly for the use of emergency service personnel but a driver also needs to know its meaning. The card shown below can be used to decode and interpret emergency Action Codes, sometimes called Hazchem Codes.

Example: The product is Oleum.
Emergency Action Code is 4WE

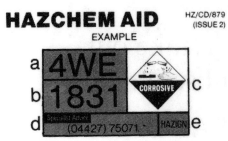

a = Hazchem code b = Product Identification number
c = Hazard Warning Diamond d = Specialist Advice:
(Telephone Number) e = Company Name or Logo

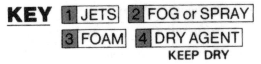

P	V	FULL	
R			DILUTE
S	V	BA	SPILLAGE
S		BA for FIRE only	
T		BA	
T		BA for FIRE only	
W	V	FULL	
X			CONTAIN
Y	V	BA	SPILLAGE
Y		BA for FIRE only	
Z		BA	
Z		BA for FIRE only	

E	CONSIDER EVACUATION

4 equates to a dry agent, i.e. the Fire Service are instructed to dispense dry agents onto the spillage or fire.

W has a "V" annotation so the product can be subject to violent or explosive reaction. Full protective clothing should be worn in the event of an incident and any spillage should be contained, i.e. not washed into drains or rivers.

E means the police should consider evacuating the area. This will depend on assessment of the circumstances by the senior policeman at the scene.

Notes for Guidance

E - First priority, Any doubt, evacuate immediate vicinity, request police assistance.

V - Can be violently or even explosively reactive.

FULL - Total body protection + Breathing apparatus.

BA - Breathing apparatus + protective gloves.

DILUTE - May be washed into DRAINS with large quantities of water.

CONTAIN - Prevent the spillage by dry earth or sand from entering drains or water courses.

HAZARD WARNING DIAMONDS :

Self - explanatory except -

harmful substances keep away from foods

other or several hazardous substances

HAZIGN are specialists in the design and production of SIGNS for Transport and Buildings. Our range includes Display holders and interchangeable panels: self-adhesive, stove enamelled, embossed and reflective signs.

HAZIGN PRODUCTS LTD

Corbiére House, Bourne End Lane, Hemel Hempstead. Herts. HP1 2RN.

Telephone: Berkhamsted (04427) 75071.
Telex: 925859.

Pressurised Tanks

THERE have been many accidents and a few deaths resulting from serious incidents with pressurised road tankers. It is imperative that any driver conveying a load to be discharged under pressure follows some simple rules to protect himself and others.

These are, before pressurising a road tank, ensure:—

- Pressure gauge is serviceable.
- Pressure relief valves are efficient.
- Compressor line is clear.
- Filter element is serviceable.
- Man-lid rings are in good condition.
- Man-lids are secured by all clamps.
- When tank is pressurised:
- Do not tighten or loosen lid clamps or flex couplings.
- Do not leave vehicle unattended, except when tank is left for overnight steaming/cleaning and steamer/fitter has been notified.
- Do not use industrial air lines unless pressure can be safely regulated.
  Important rules:
- Remember tanks under pressure are dangerous and can be lethal.
- When releasing pressure use only blow-off taps or outlet valves.
- With toxic, dangerous or irritant fumes use extreme caution and appropriate personal protection.
- If ever in doubt telephone your depot and seek advice.

NEVER TAKE SHORT CUTS WITH PRESSURISED TANKS

Entry into Road Tanks/Tank Containers

SECTION 30 of The Factories Act 1961 applies when any person is required to enter a confined space, such as a road tanker or tank container, in which dangerous fumes are liable to be present in a quantity such that it creates a risk.

No person shall enter or remain in a confined space unless:—

- He is wearing suitable breathing appartus.
- He has been authorised to enter by a responsible person, and, where practicable.
- He is wearing a belt with rope securely attached.
- There is a person keeping watch outside who is capable of pulling him out of the tank.

A road tanker/tank container shall not be considered safe to enter unless:—

- Effective steps have been taken to prevent dangerous fumes entering.
- Any sludge or similar deposit liable to give off dangerous fumes has been removed.
- The tank has been adequately ventilated and tested for dangerous fumes.
- An adequate supply of air is available for respiration.

Apart from all the above, suitable resuscitation equipment and medical oxygen must be available for use in an emergency. All equipment, breathing apparatus, etc. connected with tank entry authorisation and procedures must be examined at least monthly and records kept of these checks by a competent person.

Delivery of Petroleum Spirit

DELIVERIES of petroleum spirit are in scope to The Dangerous Substances (Conveyance by Road in Road Tankers and Tank Containers) Regulations 1981. Schedule 4 of those regulations lays down the rules for the unloading of petroleum spirit at filling stations and certain other premises licensed for storage of that substance.

At such places the following must apply:—

- Each tank must be marked in order to identify it from any other at the installation. The number must be marked in such a manner that it cannot be easily altered or obliterated.
- Each tank shall have a dipstick or some other device with which to ascertain the correct amount in the tank. It too, should bear the same number as the tank to which it relates.
- Where a pipe links the storage tank to the filling point it also must be marked in a similar manner to the storage tank.
  The Licensee must ensure that a competent person is in attendance before delivery is started and that person, who must be someone other than the driver or his attendant, will be in charge.
  The competent person must ensure that no product is spilled and to that end must:
- Confirm that there is sufficient space in the receiving tank to accept the stated quantity to be delivered.
- Ensure all connections have been properly made and all pipe work and hoses are in good order and condition.

- Ensure that the opening for the dip pipe has been securely closed.

  If all the above has been complied with a certificate (see example opposite) can be signed authorising delivery. The certificate is designed to ensure that product is delivered safely into the correct storage tank.

It must be used at all filling stations and at other premises where the amount stored does not exceed 100,000 litres. Before delivery is started the person in charge shall on each of two certificates enter in column one, the number of the tank to be filled, and in column two the amount and grade of petroleum spirit which is to be delivered. The two certificates must then be signed in the presence of the driver delivering the petroleum spirit.

- The competent person must give one copy of the signed certificate to the driver whose employer shall retain it for no less than six months. The second certificate must be held by the Licensee for a similar period.
- The competent person shall keep watch on the receiving tank throughout the discharge period.
- The driver shall keep watch on the road tank from which the petroleum spirit is being delivered.
- The engine of the vehicle or any auxiliary engine on the vehicle must not be run throughout the discharge period.

Form of Certificate

The Dangerous Substances (Conveyance by Road in Road Tankers
and Tank Containers) Regulations 1981

Address of Premises

....

....

Name of Licensee of Premises under the Petroleum
(Consolidation) Act, 1928

....

Date .... Time ....

I certify that, in accordance with Regulation 20 of and Schedule 4 to
the above-named Regulations —

(1) the storage tank identified by number in the first column below
has just been tested and the quantity of petroleum-spirit mentioned
opposite thereto in the second column can safely be received by
that tank;

(2) the connecting hose is properly and securely connected to the
filling point of that tank.

First Column	Second Column	Third Column
Storage tank number	Quantity and grade of petroleum-spirit proposed to be delivered	Signature

Note: The person in charge of the storage tank identified by number in
the first column of this certificate must enter in the second column
opposite thereto the quantity and grade of petroleum-spirit which is to
be delivered, and must sign his name in the third column opposite
thereto after the hose has been connected to that tank and before
delivery of petroleum-spirit into that tank is begun.

Conveyance of LPG
(Liquefied Petroleum Gas)

THE term LPG includes commercial butane and commercial propane and mixtures. Because of their particular characteristics all persons involved in the transportation of them should have an understanding of their properties and how to handle them safely.

They are gases stored as liquids under pressure and in this form they are compressed into about 1/250th of their gaseous volume. Therefore, less space is needed to transport them in liquid form. A small product leakage will result in a large release of flammable gas that can produce an explosive mixture with air.

These gases are heavier than air and will flow along the ground, into drains, sewers, pits, underpasses, etc. and if in contact with an ignition source, an explosion may follow. LPG comes within the scope of current conveyance regulations which set the general framework within which transportation by road takes place. The vehicle operator has responsibility for ensuring drivers are adequately trained and understand their duties as defined in law and in accordance with safe working practices.

The following is a brief summary of the most important considerations:—

● Vehicles should be constantly supervised and attended by a suitably trained, mature person except when parked.
● Park only in a safe place as defined in law and as referred to earlier in this section of the book.
● Earth the vehicle before filling and during loading and unloading operations.
● Ensure hoses and fittings are in good repair.
● Ensure vehicle is correctly marked with warning panels.
● Ensure correct Tremcard is carried in the cab.
● Ensure sufficient ullage space is allowed to cope with expansion of the LPG.
● Ensure that the vehicle is equipped with adequate fire extinguishers filled with a suitable agent. The minimum number considered to be adequate is two, both accessible from outside the cab.
● Ensure driver has guidance on how to deal with an emergency.

A typical LPG Tremcard (shown on inside back cover) gives most essential information. The relevant part of a typical Tremcard follows.

Emergency Action

Road accident or spillage

- Stop vehicle engine.
- No unsafe electrical equipment i.e. radios, etc.
- No naked lights. No smoking.
- Turn electrical master switch OFF if without risk.
- Shut off leaks if without risk.
- Keep public away from possible danger area.
- Contain leaking liquid with sand or earth.
- Prevent liquid entering drains, basements and workpits.
- Vapour may create a flammable atmosphere.
- If substance has entered a water course or drain or has contaminated soil or vegetation, inform Police.

Fire

- If exposed to fire, keep vehicle tank cool by water spray.
- Do not extinguish a leaking gas flame unless absolutely necessary.
- Consult an expert for advice on whether or not to extinguish using dry chemical or foam.
- Do not use water jet.

First aid

- Remove contaminated clothing immediately.
- Seek immediate medical treatment when anyone has symptoms apparently due to inhalation or contact with skin or eyes.

Disposal of hazardous and special wastes

MANY waste products arising directly from industrial activity are potentially harmful to humans, wildlife or the environment. Drivers are required to both understand the controls that apply and the precautions required in law.

There are two distinct themes to this problem. One deals with the actual disposal of dangerous wastes and the other with their conveyance on public roads. Taking the latter problem first, both liquid and solid wastes are covered by the following laws:—

(a) The Dangerous Substances (Conveyance by Road in Road Tankers and Tank containers) Regulations 1981, when liquids are carried in a coventional tanker, or
(b) The Road Traffic (Carriage of Dangerous Substances in Packages, etc.) Regulations 1986, when carried in drums or similar containers on a flat-bed vehicle. This

law also covers wastes such as asbestos when loaded on a tipper lorry.

Guidance on these laws is given in Sections 2 and 3 of this book, but additionally the sites where dangerous wastes can be deposited are limited under the following regulations:—

(a) River (Prevention of Pollution) Act 1951, which says that an offence will be committed if a person knowingly permits material to enter rivers and streams, etc, if pollution will be the result.

(b) Deposit of Poisonous Waste Act 1972, which prevents poisonous or noxious substances that could give rise to health risks, environmental pollution or contaminating a water supply, being disposed of in an uncontrolled manner. There is a requirement to notify the local Waste Disposal Authority of intention to dispose of wastes that can cause the problems outlined above.

(c) Control of Pollution Act 1974, which prevents "controlled wastes" such as household, industrial and commercial wastes being deposited anywhere other than at a licensed disposal site.

(d) Control of Pollution (Special Waste) Regulations 1980, which defines special wastes and introduces particular controls for them. These are defined, for instance, as:—

acids and alkalis
arsenic compounds
asbestos
copper compounds
lead compounds
mercury compounds

and many other similar materials.

If they are

1. dangerous to life
2. have a flash point of 21 degrees C or less, or
3. are medicinal compounds subject to prescription

particular procedures have to be followed by producers of the waste, the carrier of it and by the organisation that accepts it for disposal. A typical consignment note used for the carriage and disposal of dangerous waste is as shown opposite.

County Council

Serial No:	
Directive No:	
Producers Ref. No:	

CONSIGNMENT NOTE FOR THE CARRIAGE & DISPOSAL OF HAZARDOUS WASTES

Producer's Certificate A	(1) The material described in B is to be collected from .... and (2) taken to .... Signed .... Name .... On behalf of .... Position .... Address and telephone .... Date .... Estimated date of collection ....
Description of the Waste B	(1) General description and physical nature of waste (2) Relevant chemical and biological components and maximum concentrations (3) Quantity of waste and size, type and number of containers (4) Process(es) from which waste originated
Carrier's Collection Certificate C	I certify that I collected the consignment of waste and that the information given in A(1) & (2) and B(1) & (3) is correct, subject to any amendment listed in this space: I collected this consignment on .... at .... hours Signed .... Name .... Vehicle Registration No On behalf of .... Address and telephone .... Date ....
Producer's Collection Certificate D	I certify that the information given in B & C is correct and that the carrier was advised of appropriate precautionary measures. Signed .... Name .... Telephone .... Date ....
Disposer's Certificate E	I certify that Waste Disposal Licence No .... issued by .... County/ District Council, authorises the treatment/disposal at this facility of the waste described in B (and as amended where necessary at C). Name and address of facility .... This waste was delivered in vehicle (Reg No) .... at .... hours on (date) .... and the carrier gave his name as .... on behalf of .... Proper instructions were given that the waste should be taken to .... Signed .... Name .... Position .... Date .... on behalf of ....

Quick Reference Check List for Tank Cleaning Procedures

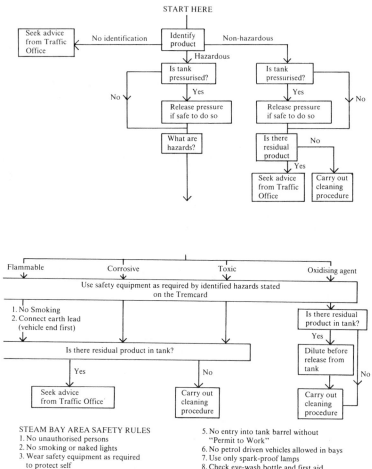

STEAM BAY AREA SAFETY RULES
1. No unauthorised persons
2. No smoking or naked lights
3. Wear safety equipment as required to protect self
4. All vehicles to be earthed
5. No entry into tank barrel without "Permit to Work"
6. No petrol driven vehicles allowed in bays
7. Use only spark-proof lamps
8. Check eye-wash bottle and first aid equipment available

SECTION 3

The Road Traffic (Carriage of Dangerous Substances in Packages, etc.) Regulations 1986
(Effective from 6th April 1987)

THE Regulations are supported by supplementary documents (a) Approved Code of Practice (b) guidance note (c) Approved List of Dangerous Substances available from HMSO. The significant point to make about the Code of Practice is that while it is not legislation in itself, it is admissible as evidence in court and may well serve as proof of failure to comply with the regulations.

When do regulations apply?

When:—
- UN packing Group 1 substances (high risk).
- Toxic gases.
- Flammable gases.
- Organic peroxides.
- Asbestos, or
- Special waste asbestos.

Are conveyed in receptacles with a capacity of 5 litres (1.1 gallons) or more

When:—
- Self reactive organic peroxides or flammable solids which have to be conveyed at controlled temperatures. (These products are listed in Schedules 2 and 3 of the regulations), or
- Dangerous substances in small tank containers, freight containers, tipper lorries, etc.

Are conveyed in any quantity

When:—
- Any other dangerous substance (medium risk).

Is conveyed in a receptacle with a capacity of 200 litres (44 gallons) or more, and when:—
- Notionally empty receptacles are conveyed.

Regulations do not apply to:
- UN Packing Group 3 substances (low risk).
- Substances used to operate the vehicle, i.e. LPG (in those

cases one spare cylinder may be carried but if this quantity is exceeded the regulations apply).
- Traffic moving under ADR.
- Some road construction vehicles.
- Vehicles engaged on agricultural work provided the substance is diluted and ready for use.

Construction
- Vehicle or freight container must be suitable for the load.
- Operator must have regard to the properties and quantity of dangerous goods to be conveyed when assessing suitability of vehicle.

Labelling of packages, etc.
Precise detail contained in the Classification, Packaging and Labelling Regulations 1984.

What is a dangerous substance?
Those substances shown in the Approved List which are:—
- Toxic or flammable gases.
- Organic peroxides.
- Substances allocated to UN Packing Group 1 and 2 i.e. high and medium danger products respectively.
- Asbestos in any form specified in the approved list.
- Asbestos waste within the scope of special waste regulations.
- Some other hazardous wastes.
- Substances not named in the approved list but having the same characteristic properties as those that are listed.

What is conveyance?
- Conveyance is taking place from the time that loading commences until the time when the vehicle has been unloaded and any residual (spilled) product has been removed so that it is deemed to be risk free.

Who is the vehicle operator?
- The person who holds, or is required to hold an operator's licence, as required by Section 60 of the Transport Act 1968.
- Where no such licence is required, the keeper of the vehicle.

Who is the consignor?
- The person who has duties under the Classification, Packaging and Labelling Regulations 1984 for properly labelling receptacles, packages, drums, etc.

Packaging

Consignor is responsible:—

- For ensuring the receptacle and associated packagings are suitably designed, constructed, maintained and closed so that there will be no spillage during normal handling.
- For ensuring the receptacles and packagings are weather resistant.
- For ensuring the receptacles and packagings will not react to the product contained in them.
- For ensuring the receptacle is capable of being securely re-closed if necessarily opened for removal of some of the products only.

What is a receptacle?

- The actual container for the dangerous substance which is in contact with it.
- This may be a 200 litre drum stacked on a vehicle.
- It could be a similar container packed with others in a crate.
- A single palletised load, etc.

There are two types of labels:

- Supply label, to provide information for the product user.
- Conveyance label, which can be used to comply with "instructions in writing" requirement instead of using Tremcard (or equivalent) given certain circumstances.

The conveyance label must display following information:—

- Product name.
- Product identification number.
- Appropriate hazard diamond.
- Nature of danger(s) inherent in the product.
- Action to be taken in emergency.
- Name, address and telephone number of consignor or some other organisation where specialist advice can be obtained in the event of an emergency.

Note: Do not confuse package conveyance labels with vehicle marking panels.

Information in writing

Operator responsible for:—

- Providing (or arranging for someone else to provide) the driver with Tremcard (or equivalent) before loading of the vehicle commences. Information required on Tremcard (or equivalent) is the same as that listed above against "conveyance label", plus advice on segregation from other products carried on the vehicle.
- Providing somewhere e.g. a clipboard for driver to display Tremcard (or equivalent) in a prominent position in the cab.

- Providing a secure and clearly marked container for driver to store Tremcards (or equivalent) not in use, product handbook, etc.
  Driver responsible for:—
- Displaying Tremcard (or equivalent) in cab while conveyance is taking place.
- Placing spare Tremcards (or equivalent), product handbooks, etc. in the "not in use" container.
- Transferring Tremcard (or equivalent) from tractor unit to trailer whenever they are detached one from the other whilst conveyance is taking place.
- Always using a Tremcard (or equivalent) for bulk loads in freight containers and tippers.

  Note: When "conveyance" labels are used instead of Tremcard (or equivalent) for complying with "instructions in writing" regulation, and no additional information is carried in the cab, packages should be loaded on the vehicle in such a way as to ensure the label can readily be seen by the emergency services personnel.

Instruction and training for drivers
Operator responsible for:—

- Ensuring the driver receives adequate instruction and training in:
    The hazards of dangerous substances his duties will require him to convey.
    Loading and unloading procedures.
    Use of safety equipment.
    Emergency procedures.
    Checks before commencing journey.
    Vehicle marking.
    Tremcards (or equivalent).
    Knowledge of relevant legislation.
- Keeping a record of training attended by a driver and making it available to the driver should he change his employment.
- Giving the driver adequate instructions on the particular load he is to convey.
- Periodic, or additional training, as necessary to comply with the regulations.

  Note: Formal training courses are not mandatory for those who only undertake local journeys involving *one* dangerous substances in small receptacles. The level for mandatory training has been set at loads of 3,000 kgs or more or for any quantity of organic peroxides of flammable solids conveyed at controlled temperatures.

Loading, stowage and unloading

All persons (operator, driver, despatchers, fork truck drivers, terminal staff, etc.) responsible for:—

- Ensuring that they do nothing contrary to the best interests of health and safety while loading, stowing or unloading a vehicle.
- Ensuring loads are firmly secured.
- Minimising risk of damage to packages.

Operators and drivers responsible for:—

- Complying with the general duties contained in the 1978 Construction and Use Regulations, namely:

- Weight distribution, packaging and adjustment of any load is such that there is no danger to other road users or persons.

- Loads are restrained such that neither danger nor nuisance is likely to be caused to property or other persons by any part falling or being blown off the vehicle.

- Ensuring packages do not project beyond the sides or back of the vehicle or above the fire screen (if fitted) if the packages contain flammable liquids or flammable gases.
- Individually securing packages with a capacity of 500 litres or more, or weighing 500 kgs or more, unless when taken as a whole they are sufficiently secure as to make the individual lashing unnecessary.
- Lashing, chocking and roping the vehicle and its load so that security is maintained after part of the load has been added or removed.
- Ensuring packages vulnerable to rain (e.g. paper sacks, fibre board cases) should be carried in a closed vehicle, in a closed container or in a curtain sided vehicle.

  Note: When wetting of the load could increase danger, e.g. with the "dangerous when wet" classification products, covering the load with tarpaulin sheet is not regarded as adequate weather protection.

Operator responsible for:—

- Agreeing a safe system of work with terminal staff for the avoidance of damage to packages during loading and unloading.

Segregation

Consignors are responsible for:—

- Informing the operator if any particular substance should

be segregated from others.

Operators are responsible for:—

- Acting on this advice and should if necessary seek expert guidance.
- Ensuring that incompatible substances are not carried together unless they can be effectively segregated against inter-reaction.

Note: Some guidance on segregation is given in the Operational Code of Practice and most of the large chemical producer companies will lay down strict rules on this subject. General guidance on segregation of products is that the following classifications should be adequately segregated or not conveyed together:

Reactive oxidising substances, including organic peroxides with oxidisable substances.

Acids with alkalis.

Substances which are liable to release toxic gases such as cycanide or hypochlorite, with acids.

Toxics with foodstuffs.

Segregation may be achieved by:—

- Additional packages, e.g. an outer drum.
- Sub-division e.g. a removable or fixed box on the vehicle non-reactive dunnage, etc.

Note: Combustible materials such as straw or wood shavings should not be used nor should any material which could react with the product.

Precautions against fire or explosion

All persons, including operator, driver, terminal staff, mechanics working on the vehicle while loaded, vehicle examiners, police, customs officers, having contact with a vehicle when conveying dangerous substances have a responsibility:

- To take precautions necessary to prevent fire or explosion.
- To take appropriate action to deal with electrical faults, engine, brake and tyre fires thereby minimising risk to the load catching alight.
- Not to use cab heaters, when conveying flammable products unless they are spark proof.
- Not to use a portable cooking stove in the cab when any dangerous substance is on the vehicle.
- To stop loading or unloading dangerous substances which could give off flammable gas or vapour when a naked light or some other potential source of ignition is in the vicinity. A thunderstorm comes under this heading.

- Not to smoke and to prevent other smokers coming close to flammable substances being loaded or unloaded.

All vehicles conveying substances should carry a minimum of 1 kg dry powder or BCF type fire extinguisher for use when dealing with vehicle fires.

Vehicles conveying the substances listed below will need more extensive fire extinguisher provision for use with small product fires. Type and size would depend on the load so advice from the consignor or some other expert should be obtained. Products to be considered in this context are:

> Flammable liquids and flammable gases.
> Strongly oxidising substances.
> Inherently unstable substances, particularly organic peroxides.
> Spontaneously combustible substances.
> Substances which in contact with water are liable to give off a flammable gas.

Fire extinguishers should be regularly maintained, in good working order and when fitted on the vehicle in a exposed position should be protected from the weather.

Loading and unloading should be carried out in a place where fire fighting equipment is available additional to that carried on the vehicle.

The operator and/or the manager of a terminal should draw up written procedures for the safe conduct of operations, clearly stating precautions to be observed. They should be made known to the driver, terminal staff and any other persons involved.

Limitation on conveyance of certain substances

The operator:—

- Must not convey substances in more concentrated form than that stated in the Approved List.
- Must ensure that when organic peroxides, self reactive organic peroxides or flammable solids are being conveyed, adequate means are available to the driver to ensure that the temperature of these substances is maintained at a safe level. Precise guidance on temperature requirement is laid down in the regulations.

The driver is responsible:—

- For ensuring any temperature criteria are met.

Note: The product groups mentioned above are subject to stringent specific controls when being conveyed. Failure to understand and consequently comply with the technical considerations necessary to prevent hazard could result in creation of extremely dangerous conditions.

Vehicle marking
The operator is responsible:—

- For providing two rectangular reflectorised orange coloured (ADR) plates, one to be fixed vertically at the front, and the other fixed vertically at the back of the vehicle when the load totals 500 kgs or more.

The Operator and the driver are responsible for ensuring the plates are:—

- Displayed throughout the conveyance.
- Kept clean and free from obstruction.

Note: The plates may remain in place if the load falls below 500 kgs as deliveries are made during a journey, but they must be removed or covered up when all dangerous substances are unloaded.

Hazard warning diamonds can still be used to supplement the ADR type plates.

Vehicle supervision
The driver is responsible for:—

- Ensuring that when the load of dangerous substance(s) reaches 3,000 kgs or more the vehicle is parked in a safe place, or
- Supervised at all times by him or some other competent person over the age of 18 years.
- For overnight stops or breaks in excess of one hour, the driver should try to use:—
  A supervised lorry park, or
  Some other place in the open air, subject to restricted access e.g. a factory or a transport depot.

It may be necessary for the operator to make prior arrangements in either case.

When it is not possible to comply with above guidance, the vehicle should be parked in a "safe place", defined as follows:
  Not a road.
  Not within 15 metres (50 feet) of occupied premises.
  Not a place where the public usually pass or gather.

The term "road" includes a lay-by but excludes:
  A disused loop road.
  Lorry parks at motorway service areas provided the distance and passing/gathering criteria are met.

- For stops of one hour or less e.g. for meals, toilet, seeking access to premises, etc., the driver should park in a place where:

> The vehicle is within sight as far as is reasonably practicable.
> The vehicle is sufficently close for him to reach it in a few minutes.

If these two requirements cannot be met, the driver should seek the assistance of some other competent person over the age of 18 years.

General points within sphere of driver responsibilities are:—

- Wherever the vehicle is parked it should be easily moved in an emergency.
- Vehicles loaded with 3,000 kgs of dangerous substances should not have the tractor unit detached from the trailer except for operational reasons at a factory or transport depot.
- If breakdown or emergency services have to be summoned he/she should stay with the vehicle and get someone else to make the call.
- Before leaving the vehicle for any reason he/she should render it and the load as secure as reasonably practicable against theft or interference.

Vehicle security

Box vans and trailers should be secured at all access points by locks fitted by the manufacturer or, failing that, locks fitted by the operator.

Freight containers should be secured by locks or container seals fitted by the manufacturer or, failing that, by the operator.

Enforcement

The enforcing authority is the Health and Safety Executive (HSE) but in most cases potential offences under these regulations will be brought to HSE notice by the police or Department of Transport Vehicle Examiners

Daily Checks and Normal Procedures

THE type of vehicles carrying small unit quantities of dangerous substances in scope to the new legislation will vary from conventional commercial flat platform vehicles to tipper lorries and vans. Therefore, while it is essential for the driver to complete a daily check on the vehicle, the content of any check is certain to vary given the many different types. However, the list below is intended to give some guidance on the main points.

Daily checks on the vehicle

Check levels and/or serviceability of the following:

> Oil.
> Coolant.
> Lights.
> Tyres.
> Wagon of trailer bed.
> Ropes or other securing devices.
> Tarpaulins and curtain sides.
> Fire extinguishers.
> Visual check for signs of corrosion.

- Before loading checks

- Vehicle/trailer bed clean.
- Identify products and quantity to be loaded from consignment or delivery note.
- Ensure Tremcard (or equivalent) is available.
- Ensure hazard warning panels are available if load is 500 kgs or more of dangerous substances in scope of the regulations.
- Ensure protective equipment as detailed on the Tremcard (or its equivalent) is available and can be taken with the driver while conveyance takes place.

At the loading point

- Report to the supervisor.
- Obey local safety rules.
- Obtain instructions for berthing the vehicle.
- Assist in loading as required.
- Wear safety equipment as detailed on Tremcard (or equivalent).
- Display Tremcard (or equivalent) in cab.
- Fit hazard warning panels if load of in scope dangerous substances is 500 kgs or more.

After loading and before departure checks

- Ensure only the Tremcard(s) (or equivalents) for load is prominently displayed in the cab and all other Tremcards are placed in a secure "Not in Use" container.
- Ensure hazard warning panels are clean and free from obstruction.
- Ensure load is correctly distributed and not overweight.
- Ensure load is secure.
- Ensure the segregation of products rule has been observed if applicable.
- Ensure no packages project beyond sides or back of vehicle.

- Ensure there are no leaks from drums, carboys, packages, etc.
- Ensure load is adequately protected from the weather.

At the discharge point
- Report to supervisor.
- Berth vehicle as instructed.
- Obey local safety rules.
- Assist in unloading as required.
- Wear safety equipment as detailed on Tremcard(s) or equivalent(s).
- Ensure any residue is cleaned from wagon or trailer bed.
- Remove hazard warning panels when load is fully discharged.
- Obtain signature for the load.

Vehicle Marking

REFERENCE to the lists of dangerous substances in Section 4 of this handbook will provide information regarding the Packing Group of most listed substance except gases. The Road Traffic (Carriage of Dangerous Substances in Packages, Etc.) Regulations 1986 bring into scope the substances shown in the Packing Groups 1 and 2 when they are conveyed in receptacles of certain capacities i.e. 5 litres in the case of Packing Group 1 and 200 litres in Packing Group 2. Packing Group 3 substances are not in scope.

It is important for a driver to understand the significance of knowing the Packing Group of substances loaded, or to be loaded, on to his vehicle because at a given quantity of material on board the vehicle hazard warning panels must be displayed.

One Hazard Warning Panel is to be mounted at the front of the vehicle and the other at the rear. The panels are orange-coloured and have the same specification as those used for ADR i.e. international dangerous goods movements in Europe when 500 kgs of dangerous substances in scope to the regulations are loaded on the vehicle. The orange plate to be displayed is illustrated on inside front cover.

When displayed the plates must be kept clean and free from obstruction. The plates may remain in place if the load falls below 500 kgs if deliveries are made during a journey, but they must be removed or covered up when all dangerous substances are unloaded.

The purpose of these orange plates is to inform the emergency services in the event of an accident that the vehicle is carrying a

43

significant amount of dangerous substances and it should be approached with caution.

In the past some vehicle operators have identified vehicles carrying dangerous substances by displaying the familiar diamond labels (see back cover). These diamonds can still be used and left permanently on the vehicles if the operator wishes but they are additional to the orange Hazard Warning Panels and not in place of them.

SECTION 4

Lists of Dangerous Substances

THE lists that follow this explanatory note have been compiled in the form of a 6-column table and the detail given is relevant to either:—

1. Bulk loads conveyed in tanks with a capacity of 660 gallons, 3,000 litres or 3 cubic metres, or
2. Loads conveyed in packages, drums, cylinders, sacks, carboys, small bulk containers, etc. of capacity less than 3 cubic metres.

Column 1	Lists names of single substances or special mixtures.
Column 2	Lists the United Nations substance identification number which is used worldwide.
Column 3	States emergency action code.
Column 4	States U.K. legislation classification which is in effect the primary hazard created by the substance. It is not, in many cases, the only hazard.
Column 5	States United Nations classification using a numerical scale and the figure decoded identifies the primary hazard. (See outside back cover).
Column 6	Apart from gases (class 2) all substances, where practicable, have been given a packing

group category according to their degree of danger.

Group 1	High risk
Group 2	Medium risk
Group 3	Low risk

When an asterisk is shown in Column 6 against a specific substance seek advice from the consignor regarding packing group.

Columns 1, 2, 3 and 4 are applicable to movements of materials in scope to The Dangerous Substances (Conveyance by Road in Road Tankers and Tank Containers) Regulations 1981.

Columns 1, 2, 4 and 6 are applicable to movements of materials in scope to The Road Traffic (Carriage of Dangerous Substances in Packages, etc.) regulations 1986.
There are 3 parts to this Section:

Part 1 — Single Substances and Specified Mixtures
Part 2 — Mixtures and Other Substances
Part 3 — Groups of Substances

LIST OF DANGEROUS SUBSTANCES AND SPECIFIED MIXTURES

PART 1 SINGLE SUBSTANCES AND SPECIFIED MIXTURES (Alphabetical)

Name of Substance 1	Substance Identification No. 2	Emergency Action Code 3	Classification for Conveyance 4	UN Class 5	Packing Group 6
Acetal	1088	3YE	Flammable Liquid	3	2
Acetaldehyde	1089	2YE	Flammable Liquid	3	1
Acetaldehyde Oxime	2332	2SE	Flammable Liquid	3	2
Acetic acid, glacial or Acetic acid solution *more than 80 percent acid, by weight*	2789	2P	Corrosive substance	8	2
Acetic anhydride	1715	2P	Corrosive substance	8	2
Acetoin	See Acetyl methyl carbinol			—	—
Acetone	1090	2 Y E	Flammable liquid	3	2
Acetone cyanohydrin	1541	2XE	Toxic substance	6.1	1
Acetone oils	1091	3YE	Flammable liquid	3	2
Acetonitrile	See Methyl Cyanide			—	—
Acetyl bromide	1716	4WE	Corrosive substance	8	1
Acetyl chloride	1717	4EW	Flammable liquid	2	2

46

Substance	Number	Code		Description	
Acetylene tetrabromide	See Tetrabromoethane		—		—
Acetylene tetrachloride	See Tetrachloroethane		—		—
Acetyl iodide	1898	2R	8	Corrosive substance	2
Acetyl methyl carbinol	2621	2S	3	Flammable liquid	3
Acid butyl phosphate	See Butyl acid phosphate		—		—
Acid mixtures, hydrofluoric and sulphuric	See Hydrofluoric acid and sulphuric acid mixtures		—		—
Acid mixtures, nitrating acid	See Nitrating acid, mixtures		—		—
Acid mixtures, spent, nitrating acid	See Nitrating acid, mixtures, spent		—		—
Acraldehyde	See Acrolein inhibited		—		—
Acrolein dimer, stabilised	2607	2S	3	Flammable liquid	2
Acrolein, inhibited	1092	2WE	3	Flammable liquid	1
Acrylamide	2074	2PE	6.1	Harmful substance	3
Acrylic acid, inhibited	2218	2PE	8	Corrosive substance	2
Acrylonitrile, inhibited	1093	3WE	3	Flammable liquid	1
Activated carbon	See Carbon, activated		—		—
Activated charcoal	See Carbon, activated		—		—
Adiponitrile	2205	3X	6.1	Harmful substance	3
Air, refrigerated liquid	1003	2PE	2	Non-flammable compressed gas	—

Name of Substance 1	Substance Identification No. 2	Emergency Action Code 3	Classification for Conveyance 4	UN Class 5	Packing Group 6
Aldehyde	See Acetaldehyde				
Aldol	2839	2R	Toxic substance	6.1	2
Alkaline corrosive battery fluid	See Battery fluid, alkali				
Alkyl aluminium halides	See Aluminium alkyl halides				
Alkyl sulphonic acids, liquid or Aryl sulphonic acids liquid, *with more than 5 percent free sulphuric acid*	2584	2X	Corrosive substance	8	2
Alkyl sulphonic acids, liquid or Aryl sulphonic acids, liquid, *with not more than 5 percent free sulphuric acid, gelling*	2586	2X	Corrosive substance	8	3
Alkyl sulphonic acids, liquid or Aryl sulphonic acids, liquid, *with not more than 5 percent free sulphuric acid, non-gelling*	2586	2R	Corrosive substance	8	3
Allyl acetate	2333	3WE	Flammable liquid	3	2
Allyl alcohol	1098	2PE	Flammable liquid	3	1
Allylamine	2334	2WE	Flammable liquid	3	1
Allyl bromide	1099	2WE	Flammable liquid	3	1

Allyl chloride	1100	3WE	Flammable liquid	3	1
Allyl chlorocarbonate	See Allyl chloroformate			—	—
Allyl chloroformate	1722	2WE	Corrosive substance	8	1
Allyl ethyl ether	2335	3WE	Flammable liquid	3	2
Allyl formate	2336	3WE	Flammable liquid	3	1
Allyl iodide	1723	2WE	Flammable liquid	8	1
Allyl isothiocyanate, inhibited	1545	3WE	Toxic substance	6.1	2
Allyltrichlorosilane, stabilised	1724	4WE	Corrosive substance	8	2
Aluminium alkyl halides	3052	4WE	Spontaneously combustible substance	4.2	1
Aluminium alkyl halides, *pure*	See Aluminium alkyl halides			—	—
Aluminium alkyl halides, solution	See Aluminium alkyl halides			—	—
Aluminium alkyls	3051	4WE	Spontaneously combustible substance	4.2	1
Aluminium bromide, anhydrous	1725	4X	Corrosive substance	8	2
Aluminium chloride, anhydrous	1726	4X	Corrosive substance	8	2
Aluminium chloride, solution	2581	2R	Corrosive substance	8	3
Aluminium diethylmonochloride	See Aluminium alkyl halides			—	—
Aluminium ferrosilicon powder	1395	4Y	Substance which in contact with water emits flammable gas	4.3	2

49

Name of Substance 1	Substance Identification No. 2	Emergency Action Code 3	Classification for Conveyance 4	UN Class 5	Packing Group 6
Aluminium nitrate	1438	1S	Oxidising substance	5.1	3
Aluminium powder, coated with 20 percent or more of material with a particle size of less than 250 microns	1309	4Z	Flammable solid	4.1	3
Aluminium triethyl	See Aluminium alkyls			—	—
Aluminium trimethyl	See Aluminium alkyls			—	—
Aminobenzene	See Aniline			—	—
Aminobutane	See n–Butylamine			—	—
2-Amino-4-chlorophenol	2673	2X	Toxic substance	6.1	2
2-(2-Aminoethoxy) ethanol	3055	2T	Corrosive substance	8	3
N-Aminoethyl piperazine	2815	2R	Corrosive substance	8	3
1-Amino-2-nitrobenzene	See Nitroanilines (o-, m-, p-)			—	—
1-Amino-3-nitrobenzene	See Nitroanilines (o-, m-, p-)			—	—
1-Amino-4-nitrobenzene	See Nitroanilines (o-, m-, p-)			—	—
Aminophenols (o-, m-, p-)	2512	2X	Harmful substance	6.1	3
Ammonia, anhydrous, liquefied, or Ammonia solutions specific gravity less than 0.880 at 15°C in water, with more than 50 percent ammonia	1005	2PE	Toxic gas	2	—

Name	UN No.	Code	Description	Class	
Ammonia solutions specific gravity between 0.880 and 0.957 at 15°C in water, with not more than 35 percent but more than 10 percent ammonia	2672	2P	Corrosive substance	8	3
Ammonia solutions specific gravity less than 0.880 at 15°C in water, with more than 35 percent but nor more than 50 percent ammonia	2073	2PE	Toxic gas	2	—
Ammonium arsenate	1546	2X	Toxic substance	6.1	2
Ammonium bichromate	See Ammonium dichromate			—	—
Ammonium bifluoride	See Ammonium hydrogen fluoride and Ammonium hydrogen flouride, solution			—	—
Ammonium bisulphate	See Ammonium hydrogen sulphate			—	—
Ammonium dichromate	1439	2X	Oxidising substance	5.1	2
Ammonium dinitro-o-cresolate, aqueous solutions	1843	2W	Toxic substance	6.1	2
Ammonium fluoride	2505	2X	Harmful substance	6.1	3
Ammonium fluorosilicate	2854	1Z	Harmful substance	6.1	3
Ammonium hydrogen fluoride	1727	2X	Corrosive substance	8	2
Ammonium hydrogen fluoride, solution	2817	2R	Corrosive substance	8	2
Ammonium hydrogen sulphate	2506	2R	Corrosive substance	8	3

Name of Substance 1	Substance Identification No. 2	Emergency Action Code 3	Classification for Conveyance 4	UN Class 5	Packing Group 6
Ammonium metavanadate	2859	1Z	Toxic substance	6.1	2
Ammonium nitrate, liquid *hot concentrated solution with not more than 93 percent ammonium nitrate, subject to the special condition*	2426	1P	Oxidising substance	5.1	Note: Bulk conveyance only. Transport of the substance should be prohibited except with special authorisation from a competent authority
Ammonium polysulphide, solution	2818	2X	Corrosive substance	8	2
Ammonium polyvanadate	2861	1Z	Toxic substance	6.1	2
Ammonium silicofluoride	See Ammonium fluorosilicate			—	—
Amyl acetates	1104	3Y	Flammable liquid	3	2
Amyl acid phosphate	2819	3X	Corrosive substance	8	3
Amyl alcohols, primary *or* secondary	1105	3Y	Flammable liquid	3	2
tert-Amyl alcohol	1105	2S E	Flammable liquid	3	—
Amyl aldehyde	See Valeraldehyde			—	—
Amylamine	1106	2PE	Flammable liquid	3	2
Amyl butyrates	2620	3Y	Flammable liquid	3	3
Amyl chloride	1107	3Y E	Flammable liquid	3	2
n-Amylene	1108	3Y E	Flammable liquid	3	1

Amyl formates	1109	3 Y	Flammable liquid	3	2
Amyl mercaptan	1111	3WE	Flammable liquid	3	2
Amyl methyl ketone	1110	3 Y	Flammable liquid	3	3
Amyl nitrate	1112	3 Y	Flammable liquid	3	2
Amyl nitrate	1113	3 Y E	Flammable liquid	3	2
Amyltrichlorosilane	1728	4XE	Corrosive substance	8	2
Anaesthetic ether	See Diethyl ether			—	—
Aniline	1547	3X	Toxic substance	6.1	2
Aniline chloride	See Aniline hydrochloride			—	—
Aniline hydrochloride	1548	2Z	Harmful substance	6.1	3
Aniline oil	See Aniline			—	—
Aniline salt	See Aniline hydrochloride			—	—
Anisidines	2431	3X	Harmful substance	6.1	3
Anisole	2222	3Y	Flammable liquid	3	3
Anisoyl chloride	1729	2X	Corrosive substance	8	2
Antimonious chloride	See Antimony trichloride			—	—
Antimony lactate	1550	2Z	Harmful substance	6.1	3
Antimony pentachloride, liquid	1730	4X	Corrosive substance	8	2
Antimony pentachloride, solution	1731	2X	Corrosive substance	8	2

Name of Substance 1	Substance Identification No. 2	Emergency Action Code 3	Classification for Conveyance 4	UN Class 5	Packing Group 6
Antimony pentafluoride	1732	4WE	Corrosive substance	8	2
Antimony perchloride	See Antimony pentachloride				
Antimony potassium tartrate	1551	2X	Harmful substance	6.1	3
Antimony, powder	2871	2Z	Harmful substance	6.1	3
Antimony trichloride	1733	4WE	Corrosive substance	8	2
Antu	See Naphthylthiourea				
Argon, refrigerated liquid	1951	2RE	Non-flammable compressed gas	2	—
Arsenic acid, liquid	1553	2X	Toxic substance	6.1	1
Arsenic chloride	See Arsenic trichloride				
Arsenic pentoxide	1559	2X	Toxic substance	6.1	2
Arsenic trichloride	1560	2X	Toxic substance	6.1	1
Arsenic trioxide	1561	2Z	Toxic substance	6.1	2
Arsenious chloride	See Arsenic trichloride				
Arsenous chloride	See Arsenic trichloride				
Aryl sulphonic acids, liquid	See the three entries for Alkyl or Aryl sulphonic acids, liquid				
Aviation Jet Al Fuel	See Kerosene				

Barium chlorate, solution	1445	2YE	Oxidising substance	5.1	2
Barium oxide	1884	2Z	Harmful substance	6.1	3
Barium perchlorate, solution	1447	2W	Oxidising substance	5.1	2
Battery fluid, acid	2796	2R	Corrosive substance	8	2
Battery fluid, alkali	2797	2R	Corrosive substance	8	2
Benzene	1114	3WE	Flammable liquid	3	2
Benzene sulphonyl chloride	2225	2X	Corrosive substance	6.1	3
1, 4-Benzenediole	See Hydroquinone			—	—
Benzenethiol	See Phenyl mercaptan			—	—
Benzol	See Benzene			—	—
Benzolene	See Petroleum spirit			—	—
Benzonitrile	2224	3X	Toxic substance	6.1	2
Benzoquinone	2587	2Z	Toxic substance	6.1	2
Benzosulphochloride	See Benzene sulphonyl chloride			—	—
Benzotrichloride	2226	2X	Corrosive substance	8	2
Benzotrifluoride	2338	2YE	Flammable liquid	3	2
Benzoyl chloride	1736	2X	Corrosive substance	8	2
Benzyl bromide	1737	2X	Toxic substance	6.1	2
Benzyl chloride	1738	2W	Toxic substance	6.1	2

Name of Substance 1	Substance Identification No. 2	Emergency Action Code 3	Classification for Conveyance 4	UN Class 5	Packing Group 6
Benzyl chlorocarbonate	See Benzyl chloroformate			—	—
Benzyl chloroformate	1739	2RE	Corrosive substance	8	1
Benzyl cyanide	See Phenylacetonitrile			—	—
Benzylidene chloride	1886	2X	Toxic substance	6.1	2
Benzyl iodide	2653	2X	Toxic substance	6.1	2
Borneol	1312	1Z	Flammable solid	4.1	3
Boron tribromide	2692	4WE	Corrosive substance	8	1
Boron trifluoride acetic acid complex	1742	4XE	Corrosive substance	8	2
Boron trifluoride diethyl etherate	2604	4WE	Substance which in contact with water emits flammable gas	4.3	2
Boron trifluoride propionic acid complex	1743	4XE	Corrosive substance	8	2
Brake fluid, *hydraulic*	1118	3Y	Flammable liquid	3	2
Bromine *or* Bromine, solution	1744	2XE	Corrosive substance	8	1
Bromine pentafluoride	1745	4WE	Oxidising substance	5.1	1
Bromine trifluoride	1746	4WE	Oxidising substance	5.1	1

Bromoacetic acid, solution	1938	2R	Corrosive substance	8	2
Bromoacetone	1569	2WE	Toxic substance	6.1	2
Bromoacetyl bromide	2513	4WE	Corrosive substance	8	2
Bromobenzene	2514	2Y	Flammable liquid	3	3
Bromobenzyl cyanides	1694	2XE	Toxic substance	6.1	1
2-Bromobutane	2339	2 Y E	Flammable liquid	3	2
Bromochloromethane	1887	2Z	Harmful substance	6.1	3
1-Bromo-2, 3-epoxypropane	See Epibromohydrin			—	—
Bromoethane	See Ethyl bromide			—	—
2-Bromoethyl ethyl ether	2340	2YE	Flammable liquid	3	2
Bromoform	2515	2X	Harmful substance	6.1	3
Bromomethane	See Methyl bromide			—	—
1-Bromo-3-methylbutane	2341	2 Y E	Flammable liquid	3	2
Bromomethylpropanes	2342	2 Y E	Flammable liquid	3	★
2-Bromopentane	2343	2 Y E	Flammable liquid	3	2
Bromopropanes	2344	2 Y E	Flammable liquid	3	2
3-Bromopropyne	2345	2WE	Flammable liquid	3	2
Bromotrifluoromethane	1009	2RE	Non-flammable compressed gas	2	—

* Check with consignor

Name of Substance 1	Substance Identification No. 2	Emergency Action Code 3	Classification for Conveyance 4	UN Class 5	Packing Group 6
Brucine	1570	2X	Toxic substance	6.1	2
Butadiene, inhibited	1010	2WE	Flammable gas	2	—
Butane *or* Butane mixtures	1011	2WE	Flammable gas	2	—
Butanedione	2346	2 S	Flammable liquid	3	2
Butane-1-thiol	See Butyl mercaptan			—	—
1-Butanol	See Butanols			—	—
Butanol, secondary	See Butanols			—	—
Butanol, tertiary	See Butanols			—	—
Butanols *other than Isobutanol*	1120	3 Y	Flammable liquid	3	★
Butanone	See Ethyl methyl ketone			—	—
2-Butenal	See Crotonaldehyde			—	—
Butene	See Butylene			—	—
But-1-ene-3-one	See Methyl vinyl ketone			—	—
2-Buten-1-ol	See Methallyl alcohol			—	—
Butyl acetates *other than Isobutyl acetate*	1123	3 Y E	Flammable liquid	3	2
Butyl acid phosphate	1718	2X	Corrosive substance	8	3

* Check with consignor

Substance	UN No.	Code	Classification		
Butyl acrylate	2348	3 Y	Flammable liquid	3	2
Butyl alcohols *other than Isobutyl alcohol*	See Butanols			—	—
n-Butylamine	1125	2WE	Flammable liquid	3	2
N-Butylaniline	2738	3X	Toxic substance	6.1	2
Butyl benzenes	2709	3 Y	Flammable liquid	3	3
n-Butyl bromide	1126	2 Y E	Flammable liquid	3	2
n-Butyl chloride	See Chlorobutanes			—	—
n-Butyl chloroformate	2743	3W	Toxic substance	6.1	2
tert-Butylcyclohexyl chloroformate	2747	3W	Harmful substance	6.1	3
Butylene	1012	2WE	Flammable gas	2	—
1, 2-Butyleneoxide, stabilised	3022	3YE	Flammable liquid	3	2
Butyl ethers	See Dibutyl ethers			—	—
Butyl ethyl ether	See Ethyl butyl ether			—	—
n-Butyl formate	1128	3 Y E	Flammable liquid	3	2
tert-Butyl isocyanate	2484	3WE	Flammable liquid	3	1
n-Butyl isocyanate	2485	3WE	Flammable liquid	3	2
Butyl mercaptan	2347	3WE	Flammable liquid	3	2
n-Butyl methacrylate	2227	3 Y	Flammable liquid	3	3

Name of Substance 1	Substance Identification No. 2	Emergency Action Code 3	Classification for Conveyance 4	UN Class 5	Packing Group 6
Butyl methyl ether	2350	3 Y E	Flammable liquid	3	2
Butyl nitrites	2351	3 Y E	Flammable liquid	3	2
Butyl phenols, liquid	2228	3 Z	Harmful substance	6.1	3
Butyl propionate	1914	3 Y	Flammable liquid	3	2
p-tert-Butyl-toluene	See Butyl toluenes			—	—
Butyl toluenes	2667	3 Z	Harmful substance	6.1	3
Butyl trichlorosilane	1747	4WE	Corrosive substance	8	2
Butyl vinyl ether, inhibited	2352	3 Y E	Flammable liquid	3	2
But-1-yne	See Ethyl acetylene			—	—
Butyraldehyde	1129	3WE	Flammable liquid	3	2
Butyric acid	2820	2R	Corrosive substance	8	3
Butyric anhydride	2739	2R	Corrosive substance	8	3
Butyrone	See Dipropylketone			—	—
Butyronitrile	2411	3WE	Flammable liquid	3	2
Butyroyl chloride	See Butyryl chloride			—	—
Butyryl chloride	2353	2PE	Flammable liquid	3	2
Butter of arsenic	See Arsenic trichloride			—	—

Name	Number	Code	Description	Class	Packing
Cacodylic acid	1572	2X	Toxic substance	6.1	2
Caesium hydroxide, solution	2681	2R	Corrosive substance	8	2
Caesium nitrate	1451	1 T	Oxidising substance	5.1	3
Cajeputene	See Dipentene			—	—
Calcium arsenate	1573	2X	Toxic substance	6.1	2
Calcium carbide	1402	4YE	Substance which in contact with water emits flammable gas	4.3	2
Calcium chlorate, solution	2429	1S	Oxidising substance	5.1	2
Calcium cyanamide *with more than 0.1 percent of calcium carbide*	1403	4YE	Substance which in contact with water emits flammable gas	4.3	3
Calcium nitrate	1454	1 T	Oxidising substance	5.1	3
Calcium perchlorate, solution	1455	1Y	Oxidising substance	5.1	2
Camphanone	See Camphor, synthetic			—	—
Camphor oil	1130	3 Y	Flammable liquid	3	3
Camphor, synthetic	2717	1 Z	Flammable solid	4.1	3
Caproic acid	2829	3 Z	Corrosive substance	8	3
Carbolic acid	See Phenol			—	—
Carbon, activated *other than activated carbon manufactured by the steam activation process*	1362	1 Z	Spontaneously combustible substance	4.2	3

Name of Substance 1	Substance Identification No. 2	Emergency Action Code 3	Classification for Conveyance 4	UN Class 5	Packing Group 6
Carbon, *animal or vegetable origin*	1361	1 Z	Spontaneously combustible substance	4.2	3
Carbon bisulphide	See Carbon disulphide			—	—
Carbon black	See Carbon, *animal or vegetable origin*			—	—
Carbon dioxide	1013	2RE	Non-flammable compressed gas	2	—
Carbon dioxide and Ethylene oxide mixtures *with more than 6 percent ethylene oxide*	1041	2PE	Flammable gas	2	—
Carbon dioxide and Ethylene oxide mixtures *with not more than 6 percent ethylene oxide*	1952	2PE	Non-flammable compressed gas	2	—
Carbon dioxide and Nitrous oxide mixtures	1015	2RE	Non-flammable compressed gas	2	—
Carbon dioxide and Oxygen mixtures	1014	2 S	Non-flammable compressed gas	2	—
Carbon dioxide, refrigerated liquid	2187	2RE	Non-flammable compressed gas	2	—
Carbon disulphide *blanketed with nitrogen or water*	1131	3WE	Flammable liquid	3	1

Carbon tetrabromide	2516	2Z	Harmful substance	6.1	3
Carbon tetrachloride	1846	2Z	Toxic substance	6.1	2
Carbon anhydride	See Carbon dioxide or Carbon dioxide, refrigerated liquid				
Carbonyl chloride	See Phosgene				
Casinghead gasoline	See Natural gasoline				
Caustic potash	See Potassium hydroxide, solution				
Caustic soda liquor	See Sodium hydroxide, solution				
Charcoal, activated	See Carbon, activated				
Charcoal, non-activated	See Carbon, *animal or vegetable origin*				
Chloral, anhydrous, inhibited	2075	2X	Toxic substance	6.1	2
Chlorate and Magnesium chloride mixture, solution	1459	2Y	Oxidising substance	5.1	2
Chloric acid, solution *not more than 10 percent chloric acid*	2626	2P	Oxidising substance	5.1	2
Chlorine	1017	2XE	Toxic gas	2	—
Chloroacetaldehyde	2232	2XE	Toxic substance	6.1	2
Chloroacetic acid, liquid	1750	2R	Corrosive substance	8	2
Chloroacetone, stabilised	1695	2WE	Toxic substance	6.1	2
Chloroacetophenone	1697	2X	Toxic substance	6.1	2
Chloroacetyl chloride	1752	4WE	Corrosive substance	8	2

63

Name of Substance 1	Substance Identification No. 2	Emergency Action Code 3	Classification for Conveyance 4	UN Class 5	Packing Group 6
Chloroanilines, liquid	2019	2X	Toxic substance	6.1	2
Chloroanisidines	2233	2Z	Harmful substance	6.1	3
Chlorobenzene	1134	2Y	Flammable liquid	3	2
Chlorobenzotrifluorides	2234	2Y	Flammable liquid	3	3
Chlorobenzyl chlorides	2235	2X	Harmful substance	6.1	3
1-Chloro-3-bromopropane	2688	2Z	Harmful substance	6.1	3
1-Chlorobutane	See Chlorobutanes			—	—
2-Chlorobutane	See Chlorobutanes			—	—
Chlorobutanes	1127	3 Y E	Flammable liquid	3	2
Chlorocresols	2669	2X	Toxic substance	6.1	2
Chlorodifluorobromomethane	1974	2RE	Non-flammable compressed gas	2	—
Chlorodifluoroethanes	2517	2WE	Flammable gas	2	—
Chlorodifluoromethane	1018	2RE	Non-flammable compressed gas	2	—
Chlorodifluoromethane and Chloropentafluoroethane azeotropic mixture (R502) *with about 49 percent chlorodifluoromethane*	1973	2RE	Non-flammable compressed gas	2	—

Chlorodimethyl ether	See Methyl chloromethyl ether			—	—
Chlorodinitrobenzene	1577	2W	Toxic substance	6.1	2
Chloroethane	See Ethyl chloride			—	—
2-Chloroethanol	See Ethylene chlorohydrin			—	—
Chloroform	1888	2Z	Toxic substance	6.1	2
Chloromethane	See Methyl chloride			—	—
Chloromethyi chloroformate	2745	2WE	Toxic substance	6.1	2
Chloromethyl ethyl ether	2354	3WE	Flammable liquid	3	2
1-Chloro-3-methylbutane	See Amyl chloride			—	—
1-Chloro-2-methylbutane	See Amyl chloride			—	—
Chloromethyl methyl ether	See Methyl chloromethyl ether			—	—
3-Chloro-4-methylphenyl isocyanate	2236	2X	Toxic substance	6.1	2
1-Chloro-2-methylpropane	See Chlorobutanes			—	—
2-Chloro-2-methylpropane	See Chlorobutanes			—	—
Chloromethylpropanes	See Chlorobutanes			—	—
3-Chloro-2-methylprop-1-ene	See Methyl allyl chloride			—	—
Chloronitroanilines	2237	2Z	Harmful substance	6.1	3
Chloronitrobenzenes	1578	2X	Toxic substance	6.1	2
Chloronitrotoluenes	2433	2X	Harmful substance	6.1	3

Name of Substance 1	Substance Identification No. 2	Emergency Action Code 3	Classification for Conveyance 4	UN Class 5	Packing Group 6
Chloropentafluoroethane	1020	2RE	Non-flammable compressed gas	2	—
Chloropentafluoroethane and Chlorodifluoromethane azeotropic mixture	See Chlorodifluoromethane and Chloropentafluoroethane azeotropic mixture				
Chlorophenates, liquid	2904	2X	Corrosive substance	8	3
Chlorophenols, liquid	2021	2X	Harmful substance	6.1	3
Chlorophenyltrichlorosilane	1753	4XE	Corrosive substance	8	2
Chloropicrin	1580	2XE	Toxic substance	6.1	1
Chloropicrin and Methyl bromide mixtures	1581	2XE	Toxic gas	2	—
Chloropicrin and Methyl chloride mixtures	1582	2WE	Toxic gas	2	—
Chloroprene, inhibited	1991	3WE	Flammable liquid	3	1
2-Chloropropane	2356	3 Y E	Flammable liquid	3	1
Chloropropanol	See Propylene chlorohydrin				
2-Chloro-1-propanol	See Propylene chlorohydrin				
3-Chloropropanol-1	2849	2T	Harmful substance	6.1	3

2-Chloropropene	2456	3 Y E	Flammable liquid	3	1
3-Chloropropene	See Allyl chloride			—	—
3-Chloroprop-1-ene	See Allyl chloride			—	—
alpha-Chloropropionic acid	2511	2R	Corrosive substance	8	3
2-Chloropyridine	2822	2X	Toxic substance	6.1	2
Chlorosulphonic acid *with or without Sulphur trioxide*	1754	4WE	Corrosive substance	8	1
Chlorotetrafluoroethane	1021	2RE	Non-flammable compressed gas	2	—
Chlorotoluenes	2238	3 Y	Flammable liquid	3	3
4-Chloro-o-toluidine hydrochloride	1579	2X	Harmful substance	6.1	3
Chlorotoluidines	2239	2X	Harmful substance	6.1	3
Chlorotrifluoroethane	1983	2RE	Non-flammable compressed gas	2	—
Chlorotrifluoroethylene	See Trifluorochloroethylene, inhibited			—	—
Chlorotrifluoromethane	1022	2RE	Non-flammable compressed gas	2	—
Chlorotrifluoromethane and Trifluoromethane azeotropic mixture (R503) *with about 60 percent chlorotrifluoromethane*	2599	2RE	Non-flammable compressed gas	2	—

Name of Substance 1	Substance Identification No. 2	Emergency Action Code 3	Classification for Conveyance 4	UN Class 5	Packing Group 6
Chromic acid, solution	1755	2X	Corrosive substance	8	2
Chromic fluoride, solution	1757	2X	corrosive substance	8	2
Chromium oxychloride	1758	4W	Corrosive substance	8	1
Chromosulphuric acid	2240	4W	Corrosive substance	8	1
Cinene	See Dipentene			—	—
Cinnamene	See Styrene monomer			—	—
Cinnamol	See Styrene monomer			—	—
Coal tar distillates, *flash point 21°C or above*	1136	3W	Flammable liquid	3	3
Coal tar distillates, *flash point less than 21°C*	1136	3WE	Flammable liquid	3	2
Coal tar naphtha	See Naphtha				
Coal tar oil	See Coal tar distillates (two entries)			—	—
Copper arsenite	1586	2Z	Toxic substance	6.1	2
Copper chlorate, solution	2721	2YE	Oxidising substance	5.1	2
Creosote salts	See Naphthalene			—	—
Cresols (o-, m-, p-)	2076	2X	Toxic substance	6.1	2
Cresylic acid	2022	2X	Toxic substance	6.1	2

Crotonaldehyde, stabilised	1143	2WE	Flammable liquid	3	2
Crotonic acid	2823	2X	Corrosive substance	8	3
Crotonic aldehyde	See Crotonaldehyde			—	—
Crotonylene	1144	3 Y E	Flammable liquid	3	1
Crude naphtha	See Naphtha			—	—
Cumene	See Isopropylbenzene			—	—
Cumyl hydroperoxide, *maximum concentration 95 percent in solution*	2116	2W	Organic peroxide	5.2	1
Cupriethylenediamine, solution	1761	2X	Corrosive substance	8	2
Cyanide solutions	1935	2X	Toxic substance	6.1	1
Cyanuric chloride	2670	2R	Corrosive substance	8	3
1, 5, 9-Cyclododecatriene	2518	3X	Harmful substance	6.1	3
Cycloheptane	2241	3 Y E	Flammable liquid	3	2
Cycloheptatriene	2603	3WE	Flammable liquid	3	2
1, 3, 5-Cycloheptatriene	See Cycloheptatriene			—	—
Cycloheptene	2242	3 Y E	Flammable liquid	3	2
Cyclohexane	1145	3 Y E	Flammable liquid	3	2
Cyclohexanone	1915	3 Y	Flammable liquid	3	3
Cyclohexene	2256	3 Y E	Flammable liquid	3	2

Name of Substance 1	Substance Identification No. 2	Emergency Action Code 3	Classification for Conveyance 4	UN Class 5	Packing Group 6
Cyclohexenyltrichlorosilane	1762	4XE	Corrosive substance	8	2
Cyclohexylamine	2357	3WE	Corrosive substance	8	2
Cyclohexyl isocyanate	2488	3W	Toxic substance	6.1	2
Cyclohexyl mercaptan	3054	3WE	Flammable liquid	3	3
Cyclohexyltrichlorosilane	1763	4XE	Corrosive substance	8	2
Cyclooctadienes	2520	3 Y	Flammable liquid	3	2
Cyclooctatetraene	2358	3 Y	Flammable liquid	3	2
Cyclopentane	1146	3 Y E	Flammable liquid	3	2
Cyclopentanol	2244	3 Y	Flammable liquid	3	3
Cyclopentanone	2245	3 Y	Flammable liquid	3	2
Cyclopentene	2246	3 Y E	Flammable liquid	3	2
Cyclopropane, liquefied	1027	2WE	Flammable gas	2	—
Cymenes	2046	3 Y	Flammable liquid	3	2
Cymol	See Cymenes				
Deanol	See Dimethylethanolamine			—	—
n-Decane	2247	3 Y	Flammable liquid	3	3
Diacetone alcohol	1148	2 S E	Flammable liquid	3	★

* Check with consignor

Name of Substance 1	Substance Identification No. 2	Emergency Action Code 3	Classification for Conveyance 4	UN Class 5	Packing Group 6
Diallylamine	2359	2PE	Flammable liquid	3	2
Diallyl ether	2360	3WE	Flammable liquid	3	2
4, 4-Diaminodiphenyl methane	2651	2Z	Harmful substance	6.1	3
1, 2-Diaminoethane	See Ethylenediamine				
Diaminopropylamine	See 3, 3-Iminodipropylamine				—
Di-n-amylamine	2841	3W	Harmful substance	6.1	3
Dibenzyldichlorosilane	2434	2X	Corrosive substance	8	2
1, 2-Dibromobutan-3-one	2648	2XE	Toxic substance	6.1	2
Dibromochloropropane	2872	2X	Harmful substance	6.1	3
1, 2-Dibromo-3-chloropropane	See Dibromochloropropane				—
Dibromodifluoromethane	1941	2Z	Other dangerous substance	9	3
Di-(n-butyl)amine	2248	3W	Corrosive substance	8	2
Dibutylaminoethanol	2873	3Z	Harmful substance	6.1	3
N, N-Di-n-butylaminoethanol	See Dibutylaminoethanol				—
Dibutyl ethers	1149	3Y	Flammable liquid	3	3
Di-tert-butyl peroxide subject to the condition set out in Note 1 below	2102	2WE	Organic peroxide	5.2	2

Name of Substance 1	Substance Identification No. 2	Emergency Action Code 3	Classification for Conveyance 4	UN Class 5	Packing Group 6
Di-n-butyl peroxydicarbonate, *maximum concentration 27 percent in solution, subject to the condition set out in Note 2 below*	2170	2W	Organic peroxide	5.2	2
Dichloroacetic acid	1764	2R	Corrosive substance	8	2
1, 3-Dichloroacetone	2649	2WE	Toxic substance	6.1	2
Dichloroacetyl chloride	1765	4WE	Corrosive substance	8	2
Dichloroanilines	1590	2X	Toxic substance	6.1	2
o-Dichlorobenzene	1591	2Z	Harmful substance	6.1	3
p-Dichlorobenzene	1592	2Z	Harmful substance	6.1	3
Dichlorodifluoromethane	1028	2RE	Non-flammable compressed gas	2	—
Dichlorodifluoromethane and Difluoroethane azeotropic mixture (R 500) *with about 74 percent dichlorodifluoromethane*	2602	2RE	Flammable gas	2	—
1, 1-Dichloroethane	2362	2YE	Flammable liquid	3	2
1, 2-Dichloroethane	See Ethylene dichloride			—	—
Dichlorethylene	1150	3YE	Flammable liquid	3	2

Dichloroethyl ether	1916	2W	Toxic substance	6.1	2
Dichlorofluoromethane	1029	2RE	Non-flammable compressed gas	2	—
alpha-Dichlorohydrin	See 1, 3-Dichloropropan-2-ol			—	—
Dichloroisopropyl ether	2490	2Z	Toxic substance	6.1	2
Dichloromethane	1593	2Z	Harmful substance	6.1	3
1, 1-Dichloro-1-nitroethane	2650	2Y	Toxic substance	6.1	2
Dichloropentanes	1152	3 Y	Flammable liquid	3	2
Dichlorophenols	See Chlorophenols, liquid			—	—
Dichlorophenyl isocyanates	2250	2X	Toxic substance	6.1	2
Dichlorophenyltrichlorosilane	1766	4XE	Corrosive substance	8	2
1, 3-Dichloropropanol-2	2750	2X	Toxic substance	6.1	2
Dichloropropene	2047	2W	Flammable liquid	3	2
Dichlorotetrafluoroethane	1958	2RE	Non-flammable compressed gas	2	—
1, 4-Dicyanobutane	See Adiponitrile			—	—
Dicycloheptadiene	2251	3 Y E	Flammable liquid	3	2
Dicyclohexylamine	2565	3X	Corrosive substance	8	3
Dicyclopentadiene	2048	3 Y	Flammable liquid	3	2
1, 2-Di-(dimethylamino) ethane	2372	3WE	Flammable liquid	3	2

Name of Substance 1	Substance Identification No. 2	Emergency Action Code 3	Classification for Conveyance 4	UN Class 5	Packing Group 6
1, 2-Diethoxyethane	See Ethylene glycol diethyl ether			—	—
Diethoxymethane	2373	3 Y E	Flammable liquid	3	2
3, 3-Diethoxypropene	2374	3 Y E	Flammable liquid	3	2
Diethyl aluminium chloride	See Aluminium alkyl halides			—	—
Diethylamine	1154	2WE	Flammable liquid	3	2
Diethyl aminopropylamine	2684	2P	Corrosive substance	8	3
N, N-Diethyl aniline	2432	3X	Harmful substance	6.1	3
Diethyl carbonate	2366	3Y	Flammable liquid	3	2
Diethyldichlorosilane	1767	4WE	Corrosive substance	8	2
Diethylenetriamine	2079	2X	Corrosive substance	8	2
Diethyl ether	1155	3YE	Flammable liquid	3	1
N, N-Diethylethylene diamine	2685	2P	Corrosive substance	8	2
Di-(2-ethyl hexyl) peroxydicarbonate *Maximum concentration 45 percent solution subject to the temperature not exceeding −15°C*	2123	2W	Organic peroxide	5.2	2
Di-(2-ethylhexyl) phosphoric acid	See Disooctyl acid phoshate			—	
Diethyl Ketone	1156	3 Y E	Flammable liquid	3	2

Name	UN No.	Class	Hazard	Col1	Col2
Diethylmagnesium	See Magnesium alkyls			—	—
Diethyl sulphate	1594	2X	Toxic substance	6.1	1
Diethyl sulphide	2375	3YE	Flammable liquid	3	2
Diethylthiophosphoryl chloride	2751	2R	Corrosive substance	8	2
Diethylzinc	1366	4WE	Spontaneously combustible substance	4.2	1
Difluoroethane	1030	2WE	Flammable gas	2	—
1, 1-Difluoroethylene	1959	2PE	Flammable gas	2	—
Difluoromonochloroethanes	See Chlorodifluoroethanes			—	—
Difluorophosphoric acid, anhydrous	1768	2XE	Corrosive substance	8	2
2, 3-Dihydropyran	2376	2YE	Flammable liquid	3	2
p-Dihydroxybenzene	See Hydroquinone			—	—
Diisobutylamine	2361	3WE	Flammable liquid	3	2
alpha-Diisobutylene	See Diisobutylene			—	—
beta-Diisobutylene	See Diisobutylene			—	—
Diisobutylene, isomeric compounds	2050	3 Y E	Flammable liquid	3	2
Diisobutyl ketone	1157	3 Y E	Flammable liquid	3	3
Diisooctyl acid phosphate	1902	3X	Corrosive substance	8	3
Diisopropylamine	1158	3WE	Flammable liquid	3	2

Name of Substance 1	Substance Identification No. 2	Emergency Action Code 3	Classification for Conveyance 4	UN Class 5	Packing Group 6
Diisopropylethanolamine	2825	3X	Corrosive substance	8	3
Diisopropyl ether	1159	3 Y E	Flammable liquid	3	2
Diketene, inhibited	2521	2 S	Flammable liquid	3	2
1, 1-Dimethoxyethane	2377	2 Y E	Flammable liquid	3	2
1, 2-Dimethoxyethane	2252	2 S E	Flammable liquid	3	2
Dimethoxystrychnine	See Brucine			—	—
Dimethyl acetal	See 1, 1-Dimethoxyethane			—	—
Dimethylamine, anhydrous	1032	2PE	Flammable gas	2	—
Dimethylamine, solution	1160	2PE	Flammable liquid	3	2
2-Dimethylaminoacetonitrile	2378	2W	Flammable liquid	3	2
2-Dimethylaminoethanol	See Dimethylethanolamine			—	—
Dimethylaminoethyl methacrylate	2522	2T	Toxic substance	6.1	2
N, N-Dimethylaniline	2253	3X	Toxic substance	6.1	2
Dimethyl-arsenic acid	See Cacodylic acid			—	—
2, 3-Dimethylbutane	2457	3 Y E	Flammable liquid	3	2
1, 3-Dimethylbutylamine	2379	3WE	Flammable liquid	3	2
Dimethylcarbamoyl chloride	2262	2R	Corrosive substance	8	2

Dimethyl carbonate	1161	3YE	Flammable liquid	3	2
Dimethylcyclohexanes	2263	3 Y E	Flammable liquid	3	2
Dimethylcyclohexylamine	2264	3W	Corrosive substance	8	2
Dimethyldichlorosilane	1162	4WE	Flammable liquid	3	1
Dimethyldiethoxysilane	2380	3 Y	Flammable liquid	3	2
Dimethyldioxanes	2707	3 Y	Flammable liquid	3	2
Dimethyl disulphide	2381	3YE	Flammable liquid	3	2
Dimethylethanolamine	2051	2S	Flammable liquid	3	2
Dimethyl ether	1033	2WE	Flammable gas	2	—
N, N-Dimethylformamide	2265	2P	Harmful substance	3	3
Dimethylhydrazine, symmetrical	2382	2WE	Flammable liquid	3	1
Dimethylhydrazine, unsymmetrical	1163	2WE	Flammable liquid	3	1
Dimethylmagnesium	See Magnesium alkyls			—	—
2, 2-Dimethylpropane	2044	2WE	Flammable gas	2	—
Dimethyl sulphate	1595	2XE	Toxic substance	6.1	1
Dimethyl sulphide	1164	3YE	Flammable liquid	3	1
Dimethyl thiophosphoryl chloride	2267	2X	Corrosive substance	8	3
Dimethylzinc	1370	4WE	Spontaneously combustible substance	4.2	1

Name of Substance 1	Substance Identification No. 2	Emergency Action Code 3	Classification for Conveyance 4	UN Class 5	Packing Group 6
Dinitroanilines	1596	2W	Toxic substance	6.1	2
Dinitrobenzenes	1597	2W	Toxic substance	6.1	2
Dinitrochlorobenzene	See Chlorodinitrobenzene			—	—
Dinitro-o-cresol	1598	2W	Toxic substance	6.1	2
Dinitrophenol, solution	1599	3WE	Toxic substance	6.1	2
Dinitrotoluenes, molten	1600	2W	Toxic substance	6.1	2
Dioxane	1165	2SE	Flammable liquid	3	2
Dioxolane	1166	2PE	Flammable liquid	3	2
Dipentene	2052	3Y	Flammable liquid	3	2
Diphenyldichlorosilane	1769	4XE	Corrosive substance	8	2
Diphenylmethane-4, 4'-diisocyanate	2489	2X	Harmful substance	6.1	3
Diphenylmethyl bromide	1770	2X	Corrosive substance	8	2
Dipropylamine	2383	2PE	Flammable liquid	3	2
Dipropyl ether	2384	3Y E	Flammable liquid	3	2
Dipropylene triamine	See 3, 3'-Iminodipropylamine			—	—
Dipropylketone	2710	3Y	Flammable liquid	3	3
Diquat	7003	2R	Harmful substance	—	★

* Check with consignor

Name	UN No.		Class	5.2	2
Di-(3,5,5-trimethylhexanoyl) peroxide maximum concentration 40 percent in solution, subject to the temperature exceeding 0°C	2128	2WE	Organic peroxide	5.2	2
Divinyl ether, inhibited	1167	3YE	Flammable liquid	3	2
Dodecyltrichlorosilane	1771	4XE	Corrosive substance	8	2
Epibromohydrin	2558	2W	Toxic substance	6.1	1
Epichlorohydrin	2023	2W	Toxic substance	6.1	2
Epoxyethane	See Ethylene oxide			—	—
1, 2-Epoxy-3-ethoxypropane	2752	3W	Flammable liquid	3	3
2-3-Epoxy-1-propanol	See Glycidaldehyde			—	—
2, 3-Epoxypropyl ethyl ether	See 1, 2-Epoxy-3-ethoxy-propane			—	—
Ethane, compressed	1035	2PE	Flammable gas	2	—
Ethane, refrigerated liquid	1961	2WE	Flammable gas	2	—
Ethanethiol	See Ethyl mercaptan			—	—
Ethanol *or* Ethanol solutions including Alcoholic beverages	1170	2 S E	Flammable liquid	3	★
Ethanolamine *or* Ethanolamine, solutions	2491	2R	Corrosive substance	8	3
Ether	See Diethyl ether			—	—
2-Ethoxyethanol	See Ethylene glycol monoethyl ether			—	—

* Check with consignor

Name of Substance 1	Substance Identification No. 2	Emergency Action Code 3	Classification for Conveyance 4	UN Class 5	Packing Group 6
2-Ethoxyethylacetate	See Ethylene glycol monoethyl ether acetate				
Ethoxy propane-1	See Ethyl propyl ether				
Ethyl acetate	1173	3 Y E	Flammable liquid	3	2
Ethyl acetylene, inhibited	2452	2WE	Flammable gas	2	—
Ethyl acrylate, inhibited	1917	3WE	Flammable liquid	3	2
Ethyl alcohol	See Ethanol				
Ethyl aluminium dichloride	See Aluminium alkyl halides				
Ethyl aluminium sesquichloride	See Aluminium alkyl halides				
Ethylamine	1036	2PE	Flammable gas	2	—
Ethylamine, aqueous solutions with *not less than 50 percent but not more than 70 percent ethylamine*	2270	2PE	Flammable liquid	3	2
Ethyl amyl ketone	2271	3 Y	Flammable liquid	3	3
N-Ethylaniline	2272	3X	Harmful substance	6.1	3
2-Ethylaniline	2273	3X	Harmful substance	6.1	3
Ethylbenzene	1175	3 Y E	Flammable liquid	3	2
N-Ethyl-N-benzylaniline	2274	3X	Harmful substance	6.1	3

N-Ethylbenzyltoluidines	2753	3X	Harmful substance	6.1	3
Ethyl borate	1176	2 S E	Flammable liquid	3	2
Ethyl bromide	1891	3YE	Toxic substance	6.1	2
Ethyl bromoacetate	1603	2XE	Toxic substance	6.1	2
2-Ethylbutanol	2275	3 Y	Flammable liquid	3	3
Ethylbutyl acetate	1177	3 Y	Flammable liquid	3	3
Ethyl butyl ether	1179	3 Y E	Flammable liquid	3	2
2-Ethylbutyraldehyde	1178	3YE	Flammable liquid	3	2
Ethyl butyrate	1180	3 Y	Flammable liquid	3	2
Ethyl chloride	1037	3WE	Flammable gas	2	—
Ethyl chloroacetate	1181	2WE	Toxic substance	6.1	2
Ethyl chlorothioformate	2826	2X	Corrosive substance	8	2
Ethyl crotonate	1862	3 Y E	Flammable liquid	3	2
Ethyldichloroarsine	1892	2XE	Toxic substance	6.1	1
Ethyldichlorosilane	1183	4WE	Substance which in contact with water emits flammable gas	4.3	2
Ethylene, compressed	1962	2PE	Flammable gas	2	—
Ethylene chlorohydrin	1135	2W	Toxic substance	6.1	2
Ethylenediamine	1604	2P	Corrosive substance	8	2

Name of Substance 1	Substance Identification No. 2	Emergency Action Code 3	Classification for Conveyance 4	UN Class 5	Packing Group 6
Ethylene dibromide	1605	2XE	Toxic substance	6.1	2
Ethylene dibromide and Methyl bromide mixtures, liquid	See Methyl bromide and Ethylene dibromide mixtures, liquid			—	—
Ethylene dichloride	1184	2YE	Flammable liquid	3	2
Ethylene glycol diethyl ether	1153	3 Y	Flammable liquid	3	3
Ethylene glycol monobutyl ether	2369	2R	Harmful substance	6.1	3
Ethylene glycol monoethyl ether	1171	2S	Flammable liquid	3	3
Ethylen glycol monomethyl ether	1188	2S	Flammable liquid	3	3
Ethylene glycol monomethyl ether acetate	1189	2S	Flammable liquid	3	2
Ethylene glycol monoethyl ether acetate	1172	2S	Flammable liquid	3	3
Ethylene oxide *blanketed with nitrogen*	1040	2PE	Flammable gas	2	—
Ethylene oxide and Carbon dioxide mixtures	See the two entries for Carbon Dioxide and Ethylene oxide			—	—
Ethylene, refrigerated liquid	1038	2WE	Flammable gas	2	—
Ethyl ether	See Diethyl ether			—	—

Ethyl fluoride	2453	2WE	Flammable gas	2	—
Ethyl formate	1190	3YE	Flammable liquid	3	2
2-Ethylhexylamine	2276	3W	Corrosive substance	8	3
2-Ethylhexyl chloroformate	2748	3W	Toxic substance	6.1	2
2-Ethyl hexyl perdicarbonate	See Di-(2-ethyl hexyl) peroxydicarbonate			—	—
Ethylidene chloride	See 1, 1-Dichloroethane			—	—
Ethyl isobutyrate	2385	3 Y E	Flammable liquid	3	2
Ethyl isocyanate	2481	3WE	Flammable liquid	3	1
Ethyl lactate	1192	3 Y	Flammable liquid	3	3
Ethyl mercaptan	2363	3YE	Flammable liquid	3	2
Ethyl methacrylate	2277	3 Y E	Flammable liquid	3	2
Ethyl methyl ether	1039	2PE	Flammable gas	2	—
Ethyl methyl ketone	1193	2 Y E	Flammable liquid	3	2
Ethyl orthoformate	2524	2 S	Flammable liquid	3	2
Ethyl oxalate	2525	3X	Harmful substance	6.1	3
Ethylphenyldichlorosilane	2435	4XE	Corrosive substance	8	2
1-Ethyl piperidine	2386	3WE	Flammable liquid	3	2
Ethyl propionate	1195	3 Y E	Flammable liquid	3	2
Ethyl propyl ether	2615	3 Y E	Flammable liquid	3	2

Name of Substance 1	Substance Identification No. 2	Emergency Action Code 3	Classification for Conveyance 4	UN Class 5	Packing Group 6
Ethyl silicate	See Tetraethyl silicate			—	—
Ehtyl sulphate	See Diethyl sulphate			—	—
Ethylsulphuric acid	2571	2X	Corrosive substance	8	2
Ethyltrichlorosilane	1196	4WE	Flammable liquid	3	1
Ferric arsenate	1606	2Z	Toxic substance	6.1	2
Ferric arsenite	1607	2Z	Toxic substance	6.1	2
Ferric chloride, solution	2582	2T	Corrosive substance	8	3
Ferrosilicon with 30 percent or more but less than 90 percent silicon	1408	4Z	Substance which in contact with water emits flammable gas	4.3	3
Ferrous arsenate	1608	2Z	Toxic substance	6.1	2
Fluoboric acid	1775	2X	Corrosive substance	8	2
Fluoric acid	See Hydrofluoric acid			—	—
Fluoroanilines	2941	2W	Harmful substance	6.1	3
Fluorobenzene	2387	3YE	Flammable liquid	3	2
Fluoroethane	See Ethyl fluoride			—	—
Fluoroform	See Trifluoromethane			—	—

Fluoromethane	See Methyl fluoride			—	—
Fluorophosphoric acid, anhydrous	1776	2XE	Corrosive substance	8	2
Fluorosulphonic acid	1777	4WE	Corrosive substance	8	1
Fluorotoluenes	2388	3YE	Flammable liquid	3	2
Fluosilicic acid	1778	2X	Corrosive substance	8	2
Formaldehyde, solution	1198	2SE	Flammable liquid	3	★
Formaldehyde, solution *flash point above 55°C*	2209	2T	Other dangerous substance	9	3
Formalin	See Formaldehyde, solution (two entries)			—	—
Formic acid	1779	2R	Corrosive substance	8	2
Formic aldehyde	See Formaldehyde, solution (two entries)			—	—
2-Formyl-3, 4-dihydro-2H-pyran	See Acrolein dimer, stabilised			—	—
Fumaryl chloride	1780	2P	Corrosive substance	8	2
Furan	2389	3WE	Flammable liquid	3	1
Furfuryl alcohol	2874	2R	Harmful substance	6.1	3
Furfurylamine	2526	2P	Flammable liquid	3	2
Furyl carbinol	See Furfuryl alcohol			—	—
Fusel oil	1201	3Y	Flammable liquid	3	★
Gas drips, *hydrocarbon*	1864	3YE	Flammable liquid	3	2

* Check with consignor

Name of Substance 1	Substance Identification No. 2	Emergency Action Code 3	Classification for Conveyance 4	UN Class 5	Packing Group 6
Gasoline Casinghead	See Natural gasoline			—	—
Glycerol-1, 3-dichlorohydrin	See 1, 3-Dichloropropan-2-ol			—	—
Glycidaldehyde	2622	2P	Flammable liquid	3	2
Gutta percha solution	1205	3 Y	Flammable liquid	3	2
Hazardous waste, liquid, containing acid	7006	2WE	Other dangerous substance	9	★
Hazardous waste, liquid, containing alkali	7008	2WE	Other dangerous substance	9	★
Hazardous waste, liquid, containing inorganic cyanides	7019	4X	Other dangerous substance	9	★
Hazardous waste, liquid, flammable, flash point less than 21°C	7010	3WE	Other dangerous substance	9	★
Hazardous waste, liquid, flammable, flash point 21°C or above	7011	3W	Other dangerous substance	9	★
Hazardous waste, solid, containing inorganic cyanides	7018	4X	Other dangerous substance	9	★
Hazardous waste, solid or sludge, containing acid	7007	2WE	Other dangerous substance	9	★

* Check with consignor

Hazardous waste, solid or sludge, containing alkali	7009	2WE	Other dangerous substance	9	★
Helium, refrigerated liquid	1963	2R	Non-flammable compressed gas	2	—
Heptanes	1206	3 Y E	Flammable liquid	3	2
4-Heptanone	See Dipropylketone				
n-Heptene	2278	3 Y E	Flammable liquid	3	2
Hexachlorobenzene	2729	1 Z	Harmful substance	6.1	3
Hexachlorobutadiene	2279	2X	Harmful substance	6.1	3
Hexachlorocyclopentadiene	2646	2X	Toxic substance	6.1	1
Hexachlorophene	2875	1 Z	Harmful substance	6.1	3
Hexadecyltrichlorosilane	1781	4XE	Corrosive substance	8	2
Hexadiene	2458	3 Y E	Flammable liquid	3	2
Hexaethyl tetraphosphate	1611	2X	Toxic substance	6.1	★
Hexafluoroacetone	2420	4WE	Toxic gas	2	—
Hexafluoroacetone hydrate	2552	2X	Toxic substance	6.1	2
Hexafluoroethane	2193	2RE	Non-flammable compressed gas	2	—
Hexafluorophosphoric acid	1782	2XE	Corrosive substance	8	2
Hexafluoropropylene	1858	2XE	Toxic gas	2	—

* Check with consignor

Name of Substance 1	Substance Identification No. 2	Emergency Action Code 3	Classification for Conveyance 4	UN Class 5	Packing Group 6
Hexaldehyde	1207	3 Y	Flammable liquid	3	3
Hexamethylenediamine, solution	1783	2R	Corrosive substance	8	2
Hexamethylenediisocyanate	2281	3X	Toxic substance	6.1	2
Hexamethyleneimine	2493	3WE	Flammable liquid	3	2
Hexanes	1208	3 Y E	Flammable liquid	3	2
Hexanols	2282	3 Y	Flammable liquid	3	3
1-Hexene	2370	3YE	Flammable liquid	3	2
Hexyltrichlorosilane	1784	4XE	Corrosive substance	8	2
Hydrazine, anhydrous *or* Hydrazine, aqueous solutions, *with more than 64 percent hydrazine, by weight*	2029	2PE	Flammable liquid	8	1
Hydrazine hydrate *or* Hydrazine, aqueous solutions, *with not more than 64 percent hydrazine, by weight*	2030	2P	Corrosive substance	8	2
Hydriodic acid, anhydrous	See Hydrogen iodide, anhydrous				
Hydriodic acid, solution	1787	2R	Corrosive substance	8	2
Hydrobromic acid, solution	1788	2R	Corrosive substance	8	2

Hydrochloric acid, solution	1789	2R	Corrosive substance	8	2
Hydrocyanic acid, aqueous solutions with not more than 20 percent hydrocyanic acid	1613	2WE	Toxic substance	6.1	1
Hydrofluoboric acid	See Fluoboric acid			—	—
Hydrofluoric acid and sulphuric acid mixtures	1786	4WE	Corrosive substance	8	1
Hydrofluoric acid, solution with less than 60 percent hydrogen fluoride	1790	2PE	Corrosive substance	8	2
Hydrofluoric acid, solution with 60 percent or more hydrogen fluoride	1790	4WE	Corrosive substance	8	1
Hydrofluosilicic acid	See Fluosilicic acid			—	—
Hydrogen bromide, anhydrous	1048	2RE	Toxic gas	2	—
Hydrogen bromide, solution	See Hydrobromic acid, solution			—	—
Hydrogen chloride, anhydrous	1050	2RE	Toxic gas	2	—
Hydrogen chloride, refrigerated liquid	2186	2RE	Toxic gas	2	—
Hydrogen fluoride, anhydrous	1052	4WE	Corrosive substance	2	1
Hydrogen fluoride, solution	See Hydrofluoric acid, solution			—	—
Hydrogen iodide, anhydrous	2197	2RE	Toxic gas	2	—
Hydrogen iodide, solution	See Hydriodic acid, solution			—	—

Name of Substance 1	Substance Identification No. 2	Emergency Action Code 3	Classification for Conveyance 4	UN Class 5	Packing Group 6
Hydrogen peroxide, aqueous solutions *with at least 20 percent but not more than 60 percent hydrogen peroxide (stabilised as necessary)*	2014	2P	Oxidising substance	5.1	2
Hydrogen peroxide, stabilised *or* Hydrogen peroxide, aqueous solutions, stabilised *with more than 60 percent hydrogen peroxide*	2015	2PE	Oxidising substance	5.1	1
Hydrogen, refrigerated liquid	1966	2WE	Flammable gas	2	—
Hydrogen sulphide, liquefied	1053	2WE	Toxic gas	2	—
Hydroquinol	See Hydroquinone				—
Hydroquinone	2662	2Z	Harmful substance	6.1	3
Hydrosilicofluoric acid	See Fluosilicic acid				—
3-Hydroxybutan-2-one	See Acetyl methyl carbinol				—
Hydroxylamine sulphate	2865	2R	Corrosive substance	8	3
1-Hydroxy-3-methyl-2-penten-4-yne	See 1-Pentol				—
3-Hydroxyphenol	See Resorcinol				—
Hypochlorite, solutions *with more than 5 percent available chlorine*	1791	2R	Corrosive substance	8	2

3, 3'-Iminodipropylamine	2269	2R	Corrosive substance	8	3
Iodine monochloride	1792	2PE	Corrosive substance	8	2
2-Iodobutane	2390	2 Y E	Flammable liquid	3	2
Iodomethane	See Methyl iodide			—	—
Iodomethylpropanes	2391	2 Y E	Flammable liquid	3	2
Iodopropanes	2392	2 Y E	Flammable liquid	3	2
IPDI	See Isophoronediisocyanate			—	—
Iron chloride	See Ferric chloride			—	—
Isobutane or Isobutane mixtures	1969	2WE	Flammable gas	2	—
Isobutanol	1212	3 Y	Flammable liquid	3	2
Isobutene	See Isobutylene			—	—
Isobutyl acetate	1213	3 Y E	Flammable liquid	3	2
Isobutyl acrylate	2527	3 Y	Flammable liquid	3	2
Isobutyl alcohol	See Isobutanol			—	—
Isobutyl aldehyde	See Isobutyraldehyde			—	—
Isobutylamine	1214	2WE	Flammable liquid	3	2
Isobutylene	1055	2WE	Flammable gas	2	—
Isobutyl formate	2393	3 Y E	Flammable liquid	3	2
Isobutyl isobutyrate	2528	3 Y	Flammable liquid	3	3

Name of Substance 1	Substance Identification No. 2	Emergency Action Code 3	Classification for Conveyance 4	UN Class 5	Packing Group 6
Isobutyl isocyanate	2486	3WE	Flammable liquid	3	2
Isobutyl methacrylate	2283	3Y	Flammable liquid	3	3
Isobutyl propionate	2394	3YE	Flammable liquid	3	2
Isobutyraldehyde	2045	3WE	Flammable liquid	3	2
Isobutyric acid	2529	2R	Flammable liquid	3	3
Isobutyronitrile	2284	3WE	Flammable liquid	3	2
Isobutyryl chloride	2395	2PE	Flammable liquid	3	2
Isocyanatobenzotrifluorides	2285	2X	Toxic substance	6.1	2
Isododecane	See Pentamethylheptane			—	—
Isoheptene	2287	3YE	Flammable liquid	3	2
Isohexene	2288	3YE	Flammable liquid	3	2
Isononanoyl peroxide	See Di-(3, 5, 5-trimethylhexanoyl) peroxide			—	—
Isooctene	1216	3YE	Flammable liquid	3	2
Isopentane	See n-Pentane			—	—
Isopentenes	2371	3YE	Flammable liquid	3	1
Isopentylamine	See Amylamine			—	—
Isopentyl nitrite	See Amyl nitrite			—	—

Name	UN No.	Code	Description		
Isophoronediamine	2289	2R	Corrosive substance	8	3
Isophoronediisocyanate	2290	2X	Harmful substance	6.1	3
Isoprene, inhibited	1218	3 Y E	Flammable liquid	3	1
Isopropanol	1219	2 S E	Flammable liquid	3	2
Isopropenyl acetate	2403	3 Y E	Flammable liquid	3	2
Isopropenylbenzene	2303	3 Y	Flammable liquid	3	2
Isopropyl acetate	1220	3 Y E	Flammable liquid	3	2
Isopropyl acid phosphate	1793	2X	Corrosive substance	8	3
Isopropyl alcohol	See Isopropanol			—	—
Isopropylamine	1221	2WE	Flammable liquid	3	1
Isopropylbenzene	1918	3 Y	Flammable liquid	3	2
Isopropyl bromide	See Bromopropanes			—	—
Isopropyl butyrate	2405	3 Y	Flammable liquid	3	2
Isopropyl chloride	See 2-Chloropropane			—	—
Isopropyl ether	See Diisopropyl ether			—	—
Isopropylethylene	See 3-Methyl-1-butene			—	—
Isopropyl formate	See Propyl formates			—	—
Isopropyl isobutyrate	2406	3 Y E	Flammable liquid	3	2
Isopropyl mercaptan	See Propanethiols			—	—

Name of Substance 1	Substance Identification No. 2	Emergency Action Code 3	Classification for Conveyance 4	UN Class 5	Packing Group 6
Isopropyl propionate	2409	3 Y E	Flammable liquid	3	2
Isopropyltoluene	See Cymenes			—	—
Isopropyltoluol	See cymenes			—	—
Isovaleraldehyde	See Valeraldehyde			—	—
Kerosene or Aviation Jet A1 Fuel	1223	3 Y	Flammable liquid	3	★
Krypton, refrigerated liquid	1970	2RE	Non-flammable compressed gas	2	—
Lamp black	See Carbon, *animal or vegetable origin*			—	—
Lead acetate	1616	2Z	Harmful substance	6.1	3
Lead arsenates	1617	2Z	Toxic substance	6.1	2
Lead arsenites	1618	2Z	Toxic substance	6.1	2
Lead dioxide	1872	2Z	Oxidising substance	5.1	3
Lead nitrate	1469	2Y	Oxidising substance	5.1	2
Lead perchlorate, solution	1470	2Y	Oxidising substance	5.1	2
Lead peroxide	See Lead dioxide			—	—
Lead sulphate *with more than 3 percent free acid*	1794	2X	Corrosive substance	8	2

* Check with consignor

Lead tetraethyl	See Motor fuel anti-knock mixtures			
Lead tetramethyl	See Motor fuel anti-knock mixtures			
Limonene, inactive	See Dipentene			
Liquefied gases *charged with nitrogen, carbon dioxide or air*	1058	2R	Non-flammable compressed gas	2	—
Liquefied natural gas	See Methane, refrigerated liquid			
Lithium alkyls	2445	4WE	Spontaneously combustible substance	4.2	1
Lithium hydroxide, solution	2679	2R	Corrosive substance	8	2
LNG	See Methane, refrigerated liquid			
Lye	See Sodium hydroxide			
Lythene	See Petroleum spirit			
Lythene	See Petroleum spirit			
Magnesium alkyls	3053	4WE	Spontaneously combustible substance	4.2	1
Magnesium arsenate	1622	2Z	Toxic substance	6.1	2
Magnesium chlorate, solution	2723	1SE	Oxidising substance	5.1	2
Magnesium fluorosilicate	2853	1Z	Harmful substance	6.1	3
Magnesium perchlorate, solution	1475	1Y	Oxidising substance	5.1	2
Magnesium silicofluoride	See Magnesium fluorosilicate			

Name of Substance 1	Substance Identification No. 2	Emergency Action Code 3	Classification for Conveyance 4	UN Class 5	Packing Group 6
Maleic anhydride	2215	2X	Corrosive substance	8	3
Malononitrile	2647	2X	Toxic substance	6.1	2
DL-p-Mentha-1, 8-diene	See Dipentene			—	—
p-Menthyl hydroperoxide, *maximum concentration 95 percent in solution*	2125	2W	Organic peroxide	5.2	1
Mesitylene	See 1, 3, 5-Trimethylbenzene			—	—
Mesityl oxide	1229	3W	Flammable liquid	3	2
Methacrylaldehyde	2396	3WE	Flammable liquid	3	2
Methacrylic acid, inhibited	2531	3X	Corrosive substance	8	3
Methallyl alcohol	2164	2P	Flammable liquid	3	2
Methanal	See Formaldehyde, solution (two entries			—	—
Methane, refrigerated liquid *or* Natural gas, refrigerated liquid *with high methane content*	1972	2WE	Flammable gas	2	—
Methanol	1230	2PE	Flammable liquid	3	2
2-Methoxyethyl acetate	See Ethylene glycol monomethyl ether acetate			—	—
Methoxymethyl isocyanate	2605	3XE	Flammable liquid	3	1

4-Methoxy-4-methylpentan-2-one	2293	3 Y	Flammable liquid	3	3
1-Methoxy-2-nitrobenzene	See Nitroanisole			—	—
1-Methoxy-3-nitrobenzene	See Nitroanisole			—	—
1-Methoxy-4-nitrobenzene	See nitroanisole			—	—
Methyl acetate	1231	2 S E	Flammable liquid	3	2
Methyl acetone	1232	2WE	Flammable liquid	3	2
Methyl acetylene and Propadiene mixtures, stabilised	1060	2WE	Flammable gas	2	—
beta-Methyl acrolein	See Crotonaldehyde				
Methyl acrylate, inhibited	1919	3WE	Flammable liquid	3	2
Methylal	1234	2 Y E	Flammable liquid	3	2
Methyl alcohol	See Methanol				
Methylallyl alcohol	See Methallyl alcohol				
Methyl allyl chloride	2554	3WE	Flammable liquid	3	2
Methyl aluminium sesquibromide	See Aluminium alkyl halides				
Methyl aluminium sesquichloride	See Aluminium alkyl halides				
Methylamine, anhydrous	1061	2PE	Flammable gas	2	—
Methylamine, aqueous solution	1235	2PE	Flammable liquid	3	2
Methylamyl acetate	1233	3 Y	Flammable liquid	3	3
Methyl amyl alcohol	See Methyl isobutyl carbinol				

Name of Substance 1	Substance Identification No. 2	Emergency Action Code 3	Classification for Conveyance 4	UN Class 5	Packing Group 6
Methyl amyl ketone	See Amyl methyl ketone				
N-Methylaniline	2294	3X	Harmful substance	6.1	3
Methyl bromide	1062	2XE	Toxic gas	2	—
Methyl bromide and Chloropicrin mixtures	See Chloropicrin and Methyl bromide mixtures				
Methyl bromide and Ethylene dibromide mixtures, liquid	1647	2XE	Toxic substance	6.1	1
Methyl bromoacetate	2643	2X	Toxic substance	6.1	2
3-Methylbutan-2-one	2397	3 Y E	Flammable liquid	3	2
2-Methyl-1-butene	2459	3 Y E	Flammable liquid	3	1
2-Methyl-2-butene	2460	3 Y E	Flammable liquid	3	2
3-Methyl-1-butene	2561	3 Y E	Flammable liquid	3	2
Methyl tert-butyl ether	2398	3 Y E	Flammable liquid	3	2
Methyl butyrate	1237	3 Y E	Flammable liquid	3	2
Methyl chloride	1063	2WE	Toxic gas	2	—
Methyl chloride and Chloropicrin mixture	See Chloropicrin and Methyl chloride mixture				

	UN No.	Code	Description		
Methyl chloride and Methylene chloride mixture	1912	2WE	Toxic gas	2	—
Methyl chloroacetate	2295	2W	Toxic substance	6.1	2
Methyl chloroform	See 1, 1, 1-Trichloroethane			—	—
Methyl chloromethyl ether	1239	3WE	Flammable liquid	3	2
Methylchlorosilane	2534	4WE	Substance which in contact with water emits flammable gas	4.3	1
Methyl cyanide	1648	2WE	Flammable liquid	3	2
Methyl cyclohexane	2296	3 Y E	Flammable liquid	3	2
Methyl cyclohexanone	2297	3Y	Flammable liquid	3	3
Methyl cyclopentane	2298	3 Y E	Flammable liquid	3	2
Methyl dichloroacetate	2299	2X	Harmful substance	6.1	3
Methyldichlorosilane	1242	4WE	Substance which in contact with water emits flammable gas	4.3	1
Methylene chloride	See Dichloromethane			—	—
Methylene chloride and Methyl chloride mixture	See methyl chloride and Methylene chloride mixture			—	—
p.p-Methylene dianiline	See 4,4'-Diaminodiphenyl methane			—	—
Methylene-di-(phenylene diisocyanate	See Diphenylmethane-4,4'-diisocynate			—	—

Name of Substance 1	Substance Identification No. 2	Emergency Action Code 3	Classification for Conveyance 4	UN Class 5	Packing Group 6
Methylene-di-(4-phenyl isocyanate)	See Diphenylmethane-4, 4'-diisocyanate			—	—
2,2'-Methylene-di-(3, 4, 6-trichlorophenol)	See Hexachlorophene	—			
Methyl ethyl ether	See Ethyl methyl ether			—	—
Methyl ethyl ketone	See Ethyl methyl ketone			—	—
2-Methyl-5-ethyl pyridine	2300	3X	Harmful substance	6.1	3
Methyl fluoride	2454	2WE	Flammable gas	2	—
Methyl formate	1243	2SE	Flammable liquid	3	1
2-Methylfuran	2301	3YE	Flammable liquid	3	2
Methyl glycol	See Ethylene glycol monomethyl ether			—	—
Methyl glycol acetate	See Ethylene glycol monomethyl ether acetate			—	—
5-Methylhexan-2-one	2302	3Y	Flammable liquid	3	3
Methylhydrazine	1244	2WE	Flammable liquid	3	1
Methyl iodide	2644	2XE	Toxic substance	6.1	2
Methyl isobutyl carbinol	2053	3Y	Flammable liquid	3	2
Methyl isobutyl ketone	1245	3 Y E	Flammable liquid	3	2
Methyl isocyanate or Methyl isocyanate, solution	2480	3WE	Flammable liquid	3	2

Methyl isopropenyl ketone, inhibited	1246	3WE	Flammable liquid	3	2
Methyl isothiocyanate	2477	2XE	Flammable liquid	3	2
Methyl isovalerate	2400	3 Y E	Flammable liquid	3	2
Methyl mercaptan	1064	2WE	Toxic gas	2	—
Methyl methacrylate monomer, inhibited	1247	3 Y E	Flammable liquid	3	2
Methylmorpholine	2535	2PE	Flammable liquid	3	2
Methyl orthosilicate	2606	3Y	Flammable liquid	3	1
Methylpentadiene	2461	3 Y E	Flammable liquid	3	2
Methylpentanes	See Hexanes			—	—
2-Methylpentan-2-ol	2560	3 Y	Flammable liquid	3	2
4-Methyl pentan-2-ol	See Methyl isobutyl carbinol			—	—
3-Methyl-2-penten-4-yne-ol	See 1-Pentol			—	—
Methylphenyldichlorosilane	2437	4XE	Flammable liquid	3	2
1-Methylpiperdine	2399	2WE	Flammable liquid	3	2
Methyl propionate	1248	3 Y E	Flammable liquid	3	2
Methyl propylbenzene	See Cymenes			—	—
Methyl propyl ether	2612	3YE	Flammable liquid	3	2
Methyl propyl ketone	1249	3 Y E	Flammable liquid	3	2
Methyl pyridines	See Picolines			—	—

Name of Substance 1	Substance Identification No. 2	Emergency Action Code 3	Classification for Conveyance 4	UN Class 5	Packing Group 6
Methylstyrene	See Vinyl toluene			—	—
alpha-Methylstyrene	See Isopropenylbenzene			—	—
Methyl sulphate	See Dimethyl sulphate			—	—
Methyl sulphide	See Dimethyl sulphide			—	—
Methyltetrahydrofuran	2536	2 S E	Flammable liquid	3	2
Methyl trichloroacetate	2533	2 Z	Harmful substance	6.1	3
Methyltrichlorosilane	1250	4WE	Flammable liquid	3	1
alpha-Methyl valeraldehyde	2367	3YE	Flammable liquid	3	3
Methylvinylbenzene	See Vinyl toluene			—	—
Methyl vinyl ketone	1251	2PE	Flammable liquid	3	2
MIBC	See Methyl isobutyl carbinol			—	—
Mirbane oil	See Nitrobenzene			—	—
Molybdenum pentachloride	2508	2X	Corrosive substance	8	3
Monochloroacetic acid	See Chloroacetic acid			—	—
Monochlorobenzene	See Chlorobenzene			—	—
Monochlorodifluoromethane	See Chlorodifluoromethane			—	—
Mono-ethylamine	See Ethylamine			—	—

Monopropylamine	See Propylamine				
Morpholine	2054	2P	Flammable liquid	3	2
Motor fuel anti-knock mixtures	1649	2WE	Toxic substance	6.1	1
Muriatic acid	See Hydrochloric acid				
Naphtha	2553	3YE	Flammable liquid	3	★
Nephthalene, crude *or* Naphthalene, refined	1334	2Z	Flammable solid	4.1	3
Naphthalene, molten	2304	1X	Flammable solid	4.1	3
Naptha, *petroleum*	1255	3 Y E	Flammable liquid	3	★
Naptha, *solvent*	1256	3W	Flammable liquid	3	★
Naphthylthiourea	1651	2Z	Toxic substance	6.1	2
Naphthylurea	1652	2Z	Toxic substance	6.1	2
Natural gas, refrigerated liquid *with high methane content*	See Methane, refrigerated liquid				
Natural gasoline	1257	3WE	Flammable liquid	3	2
Neohexane	See Hexanes				
Neon, refrigerated liquid	1913	2RE	Non-flammable compressed gas	2	—
Neopentane	See 2,2-Dimethylpropane				
Neothyl	See Methyl propyl ether				

* Check with consignor

103

Name of Substance 1	Substance Identification No. 2	Emergency Action Code 3	Classification for Conveyance 4	UN Class 5	Packing Group 6
Nicotine	1654	2X	Toxic substance	6.1	2
Nicotine hydrochloride *or* Nicotine hydrochloride solution	1656	2X	Toxic substance	6.1	2
Nicotine salicylate	1657	2X	Toxic substance	6.1	2
Nicotine sulphate, solid *or* Nicotine sulphate, solution	1658	2X	Toxic substance	6.1	2
Nicotine tartrate	1659	2X	Toxic substance	6.1	2
Nitrating acid, mixtures	1796	4WE	Corrosive substance	8	2
Nitrating acid, mixtures, spent	1826	2P	Corrosive substance	8	1
Nitric acid, red fuming	2032	2PE	Corrosive substance	8	1
Nitric acid, *other than red fuming*	2031	2PE	Corrosive substance	8	1
Nitric oxide and Nitrogen tetroxide mixtures	1975	2RE	Toxic gas	2	—
Nitroanilines (o-, m-, p-)	1661	2X	Toxic substance	6.1	2
Nitroanisole	2730	2Z	Harmful substance	6.1	3
Nitrobenzene	1662	2X	Toxic substance	6.1	2
Nitrobenzene	See Nitrobromobenzene				
Nitrobenzenesulphonic acid	2305	2R	Corrosive substance	8	2

104

Nitrobenzol	See Nitrobenzene				
Nitrobenzotrifluorides	2306	2X	Toxic substance	6.1	2
Nitrobromobenzene	2732	2X	Harmful substance	6.1	3
Nitrocellulose solutions, flammable with not more than 12.3 percent nitrogen, by weight, and not more than 55 percent nitrocellulose, flash point less than 21°C	2029	2 Y E	Flammable liquid	3	2
Nitrocellulose solutions, flammable with not more than 12.3 percent nitrogen, by weight, and not more than 55 percent nitrocellulose, flash point 21°C or above	2059	2 Y	Flammable liquid	3	2
Nitrochlorobenzene	See Chloronitrobenzenes				
3-Nitro-4-chlorobenzotrifluoride	2307	2X	Toxic substance	6.1	2
Nitrocresols	2446	2X	Harmful substance	6.1	3
Nitroethane	2842	2 Y E	Flammable liquid	3	3
Nitrogen dioxide, liquefied	1067	2RE	Toxic gas	2	—
Nitrogen, refrigerated liquid	1977	2RE	Non-flammable compressed gas	2	—
Nitrogen tetroxide	See Nitrogen dioxide				
Nitrogen tetroxide and oxide mixtures	See Nitric oxide and Nitrogen tetroxide mixtures				

Name of Substance 1	Substance Identification No. 2	Emergency Action Code 3	Classification for Conveyance 4	UN Class 5	Packing Group 6
Nitrohydrochloric acid	1798	2R	Corrosive substance	8	1
Nitromuriatic acid	See Nitrohydrochloric acid				
Nitrophenols (o-, m-, p-)	1663	2X	Harmful substance	6.1	3
Nitropropanes	2608	2Y	Flammable liquid	3	3
Nitrosylsulphuric acid	2308	4WE	Corrosive substance	8	2
Nitrotoluenes (o-, m-, p-)	1664	2X	Toxic substance	6.1	2
Nitroluidines (mono)	2660	2Z	Harmful substance	6.1	3
Nitrous oxide and Carbon dioxide mixtures	See Carbon dioxide and Nitrous oxide mixtures				
Nitrous oxide, compressed	1070	2R	Non-flammable compressed gas	2	—
Nitrous oxide, refrigerated liquid	2201	2RE	Non-flammable compressed gas	2	—
Nitroxylenes (o-, m-, p-)	1665	2X	Toxic substance	6.1	2
Non-activated carbon	See Carbon, *animal or vegetable origin*				
Non-activated charcoal	See Carbon, *animal or vegetable origin*				
Nonanes	1920	3Y	Flammable liquid	3	2
Nonyltrichlorosilane	1799	4XE	Corrosive substance	8	2

Octadecyltrichlorosilane	1800	2X	Corrosive substance	8	2
Octadiene	2309	3 Y E	Flammable liquid	3	3
Octafluorocyclobutane	1976	2RE	Non-flammable compressed gas	2	—
Octanes	1262	3 Y E	Flammable liquid	3	2
Octyl aldehydes	1191	3 Y	Flammable liquid	3	3
tert-Octyl mercaptan	3023	3WE	Toxic substance	6.1	2
Octyltrichlorosilane	1801	4XE	Corrosive substance	8	2
Oil gas	1071	2SE	Flammable gas	2	—
Oleum	See Sulphuric acid, fuming			—	—
Orthophosphoric acid	See Phosphoric acid			—	—
Oxalates, water soluble	2449	2X	Harmful substance	6.1	3
Oxirane	See Ethylene oxide			—	—
Oxygen and Carbon dioxide mixtures	See Carbon dioxide and Oxygen mixtures			—	—
Oxygen, refrigerated liquid	1073	2PE	Non-flammable compressed gas	2	—
1-Oxy-4-nitrobenzene	See Nitrophenols (o-, m-, p-)			—	—
Paraffin	See Kerosene			—	—
Paraldehyde	1264	2 S E	Flammable liquid	3	3

Name of Substance 1	Substance Identification No. 2	Emergency Action Code 3	Classification for Conveyance 4	UN Class 5	Packing Group 6
PCB's	See Polychlorinated biphenyls				
Pentachloroethane	1669	2Z	Toxic substance	6.1	2
Pentamethylheptane	2286	3 Y	Flammable liquid	3	3
Pentanal	See Valeraldehyde				
Pentan-2, 4-dione	2310	2 S	Flammable liquid	3	3
n-Pentane, *or* Isopentane	1265	3 Y E	Flammable liquid	3	1
1-Pentene	See n-Amylene				
1-Pentol	2705	3WE	Corrosive substance	8	2
Pentyl nitrite	See Amyl nitrite				
Perchloric acid with not more than 50 percent acid, by weight	1802	2P	Corrosive substance	8	2
Perchloric acid with more than 50 percent but not more than 72 percent acid, by weight	1873	2P	Oxidising substance	5.1	1
Perchlorobenzene	See Hexachlorobenzene				
Perchlorocyclopentadiene	See Hexachlorocyclopentadiene				
Perchloroethylene	See Tetrachloroethylene				
Perchloromethyl mercaptan	1670	2X	Toxic substance	6.1	1

	2131	Organic peroxide	2W	5.2	1
Peroxyacetic acid *maximum concentration 42 percent in solution with acetic acid or an aqueous solution of acetic acid with or without mineral acid*					
Petrol	1203	Flammable liquid	3 Y E	3	2
Petroleum crude oil	1267	Flammable liquid	3WE	3	★
Petroleum ether	See Petroleum spirit			—	—
Petroleum naphtha	See Naphtha, petroleum			—	—
Petroleum raffinates	See Petroleum distillates, NOS (Part 1B)			—	—
Petroleum spirit *flash point less than 21°C*	1271	Flammable liquid	3 Y E	3	2
Petroleum spirit *flash point 21°C or above*	1271	Flammable liquid	3 Y	3	3
Phenacyl bromide	2645	Toxic substance	2X	6.1	2
Phenetidines	2311	Harmful substance	3X	6.1	3
Phenol, solid	1671	Toxic substance	2X	6.1	2
Phenol, molten	2312	Toxic substance	2X	6.1	2
Phenolsulphonic acid, liquid	1803	Corrosive substance	2R	8	2
Phenylacetonitrile, liquid	2470	Harmful substance	3X	6.1	3
Phenylacetyl chloride	2577	Corrosive substance	2X	8	2

* Check with consignor

Name of Substance 1	Substance Identification No. 2	Emergency Action Code 3	Classification for Conveyance 4	UN Class 5	Packing Group 6
Phenylamine	See Aniline			—	—
Phenylcarbylamine chloride	1672	2X	Toxic substance	6.1	1
Phenyl chloroformate	2746	2W	Toxic substance	6.1	2
Phenyl cyanide	See Benzonitrile			—	—
Phenylenediamines	1673	2X	Harmful substance	6.1	3
Phenylethylene	See Styrene monomer			—	—
Phenylhydrazine	2572	3X	Toxic substance	6.1	2
Phenyl isocyanate	2487	3W	Toxic substance	6.1	2
Phenyl mercaptan	2337	3WE	Toxic substance	6.1	1
Phenylmercuric acetate	1674	2X	Toxic substance	6.1	2
Phenylmercuric hydroxide	1894	2X	Toxic substance	6.1	2
Phenylmercuric nitrate	1895	2X	Toxic substance	6.1	2
2-Phenylpropene	See Isopropenylbenzene			—	—
Phenyltrichlorosilane	1804	4XE	Corrosive substance	8	2
Phosgene	1076	2XE	Toxic gas	2	—
Phosphoric acid	1805	2R	Corrosive substance	8	3
Phosphoric acid, anhydrous	See Phosphorus pentoxide			—	—

Phosphorous acid, ortho	2834	2R	Corrosive substance	8	3
Phosphorus bromide	See Phosphorus tribromide				
Phosphorus chloride	See Phosphorus trichloride				
Phosphorus oxybromide	1939	4X	Corrosive substance	8	2
Phosphorus oxybromide, molten	2576	4W	Corrosive substance	8	2
Phosphorus oxychloride	1810	4WE	Corrosive substance	8	2
Phosphorus pentabromide	2691	4W	Corrosive substance	8	2
Phosphorus pentachloride	1806	4WE	Corrosive substance	8	2
Phosphorus pentasulphide, *free from yellow and white phosphorus*	1340	4YE	Flammable solid	4.1	2
Phosphorus pentoxide	1807	4W	Corrosive substance	8	2
Phosphorus sesquisulphide, *free from yellow and white phosphorus*	1341	1Y	Flammable solid	4.1	2
Phosphorus sulphochloride	See Thiophosphoryl chloride				
Phosphorus tribromide	1808	4WE	Corrosive substance	8	2
Phosphorus trichloride	1809	4WE	Corrosive substance	8	2
Phosphorus trioxide	2578	4X	Corrosive substance	8	3
Phosphorus, white *or* yellow, dry *or* under water *or* in solution	1381	2WE	Spontaneously combustible substance	4.2	1
Phosphorus white, molten	2447	2WE	Spontaneously combustible substance	4.2	1

Name of Substance 1	Substance Identification No. 2	Emergency Action Code 3	Classification for Conveyance 4	UN Class 5	Packing Group 6
Phosphoryl chloride	See Phosphorus oxychloride				
Phthalic anhydride	2214	2X	Corrosive substance	8	3
Picolines	2313	2S	Flammable liquid	3	2
Pinanyl hydroperoxide *maximum concentration 95 percent in solution*	2162	2W	Organic peroxide	5.2	1
Pindone	2472	2X	Harmful substance	6.1	3
alpha-Pinene	2368	3 Y	Flammable liquid	3	3
Piperidine	2401	2WE	Flammable liquid	3	2
Pival	See Pindone				
Pivaloyl chloride	See Trimethyl acetyl chloride				
Polychlorinated biphenyls	2315	4X	Other dangerous substance	9	2
Polystyrene beads, expandable, evolving flammable vapours	2211	3 Y	Other dangerous substance	9	3
Potassium	2257	4W	Substance which in contact with water emits flammable gas	4.3	2
Potassium arsenate	1677	2X	Toxic substance	6.1	2

Substance	UN No.	Code	Description	Class	
Potassium arsenite	1678	2X	Toxic substance	6.1	2
Potassium bifluoride, solution	1811	2X	Corrosive substance	8	2
Potassium bisulphate	See Potassium hydrogen sulphate			—	—
Potassium chlorate, solution	2427	1S	Oxidising substance	5.1	2
Potassium cyanide	1680	4X	Toxic substance	6.1	1
Potassium fluoride, solution	1812	2Z	Harmful substance	6.1	3
Potassium fluorosilicate	2655	1Z	Harmful substance	6.1	3
Potassium hydrogen sulphate	2509	2R	Corrosive substance	8	3
Potassium hydroxide, liquid	See Potassium hydroxide, solution			—	—
Potassium hydroxide, solution	1814	2R	Corrosive substance	8	2
Potassium, metal alloys	1420	4WE	Substance which in contact with water emits flammable gas	4.3	2
Potassium metavanadate	2864	1Z	Toxic substance	6.1	2
Potassium monoxide	2033	4W	Corrosive substance	8	2
Potassium perchlorate, solution	1489	2W	Oxidising substance	5.1	2
Potassium sodium alloys	1422	4WE	Substance which in contact with water emits flammable gas	4.3	1
Potassium sulphide, hydrated *with 30 percent or more water of crystallisation*	1847	2X	Corrosive substance	8	2

Name of Substance 1	Substance Identification No. 2	Emergency Action Code 3	Classification for Conveyance 4	UN Class 5	Packing Group 6
Propadiene and Methyl acetylene mixtures, stabilised	See Methyl acetylene and Propadiene mixtures, stabilised				
Propane or Propane mixtures	1978	2WE	Flammable gas	2	—
Propanethiols	2402	3WE	Flammable liquid	3	2
Propanol	1274	2 S E	Flammable liquid	3	2
Propene	See Propylene				—
Propionaldehyde	1275	2YE	Flammable liquid	3	2
Propionic acid	1848	2P	Corrosive substance	8	3
Propionic anhydride	2496	3X	Corrosive substance	8	3
Propionitrile	2404	2WE	Flammable liquid	3	2
Propionyl chloride	1815	2PE	Flammable liquid	3	2
n-Propyl acetate	1276	3 Y E	Flammable liquid	3	2
Propyl alcohol	See Propanol				—
Propylamine	1277	2WE	Flammable liquid	3	2
Propylbenzene	2364	3 Y	Flammable liquid	3	2
Propyl chloride	1278	3 Y E	Flammable liquid	3	2
n-Propyl chloroformate	2740	3WE	Flammable liquid	3	1

Propylene	1077	2WE	Flammable gas	2	—
Propylene chlorohydrin	2611	2P	Toxic substance	6.1	2
1,2-Propylenediamine	2258	2P	Corrosive substance	8	2
Propylene dichloride	1279	2YE	Flammable liquid	3	2
Propylene oxide *blanketed with nitrogen*	1280	2PE	Flammable liquid	3	1
Propylene tetramer	2850	3Y	Flammable liquid	3	3
Propylene trimer	See Tripropylene			—	—
Propyl formates	1281	3 Y E	Flammable liquid	3	2
n-Propyl isocyanate	2482	3WE	Flammable liquid	3	1
Propyl mercaptan	See Propanethiols			—	—
Propyltrichlorosilane	1816	4WE	Corrosive substance	8	2
Pyridine	1282	2WE	Flammable liquid	3	2
Prosulphuryl chloride	1817	4WE	Corrosive substance	8	2
Proxylin solution	See Nitrocellulose solutions, flammable (two entries)				
Pyrrolidine	1922	2SE	Flammable liquid	3	2
Quinol	See Hydroquinone			—	—
Quinoline	2656	3Z	Harmful substance	6.1	3
R.500	See Dichlorodifluoromethane and Difluoroethane azeotropic mixture			—	—

Name of Substance 1	Substance Identification No. 2	Emergency Action Code 3	Classification for Conveyance 4	UN Class 5	Packing Group 6
R.502	See Chlorodifluoromethane and Chloropentafluoroethane azeotropic mixture			—	—
R.503	See Chlorotrifluoromethane and Trifluoromethane azeotropic mixture				
Resorcin	See Resorcinol			—	—
Resorcinol	2876	2X	Harmful substance	6.1	3
Rosin oil	1286	3 Y E	Flammable liquid	3	3
Rubber solution	1287	3 Y E	Flammable liquid	3	★
Rubidium hydroxide, solution	2677	2R	Corrosive substance	8	2
Sand acid	See Fluosilicic acid			—	—
Selenic acid	1905	2X	Corrosive substance	8	1
Selenium oxychloride	2879	2XE	Corrosive substance	8	1
Shale oil	1288	3WE	Flammable liquid	3	2
Silicofluoric acid	See Fluosilicic acid			—	—
Silicon chloride	See Silicon tetrachloride			—	—
Silicon tetrachloride	1818	4WE	Corrosive substance	8	2
Silver arsenite	1683	2X	Toxic substance	6.1	2

★ Check with consignor

Sludge acid	1906	2P	Corrosive substance	8	2
Soda lime *with more than 4 percent sodium hydroxide*	1907	2X	Corrosive substance	8	3
Sodium	1428	4W	Substance which in contact with water emits flammable gas	4.3	1
Sodium aluminate, solution	1819	2R	Corrosive substance	8	2
Sodium amalgam	1424	4W	Substance which in contact with water emits flammable gas	4.3	1
Sodium ammonium vanadate	2863	1Z	Toxic substance	6.1	2
Sodium arsanilate	2473	2Z	Harmful substance	6.1	3
Sodium arsenate	1685	2X	Toxic substance	6.1	2
Sodium arsenite, aqueous solutions	1686	2X	Toxic substance	6.1	★
Sodium bifluoride	See Sodium hydrogen fluoride			—	—
Sodium cacodylate	1688	2X	Toxic substance	6.1	2
Sodium chlorate	1495	1SE	Oxidising substance	5.1	2
Sodium chlorate, solution	2428	1S	Oxidising substance	5.1	2
Sodium chlorite, solution, *with more than 5 percent available chlorine*	1908	2R	Corrosive substance	8	2

* Check with consignor

117

Name of Substance 1	Substance Identification No. 2	Emergency Action Code 3	Classification for Conveyance 4	UN Class 5	Packing Group 6
Sodium chloroacetate	2659	2X	Harmful substance	6.1	3
Sodium cuprocyanide, solution	2317	4X	Toxic substance	6.1	1
Sodium cyanide	1689	4X	Toxic substance	6.1	1
Sodium dimethylarsenate	See Sodium cacodylate			—	—
Sodium fluoride	1690	2Z	Harmful substance	6.1	3
Sodium hydrate	See Sodium hydroxide			—	—
Sodium hydrogen fluoride	2439	2X	Corrosive substance	8	2
Sodium hydrogen sulphate, solution	2837	2R	Corrosive substance	8	2
Sodium hydroxide, solution	1824	2R	Corrosive substance	8	2
Sodium methylate, solutions in alcohol	1289	2PE	Flammable liquid	3	2
Sodium monoxide	1825	2R	Corrosive substance	8	2
Sodium potassium alloys, solid	See Potassium sodium alloys			—	—
Sodium pentachlorophenate	2567	2X	Toxic substance	6.1	2
Sodium perchlorate, solution	1502	2W	Oxidising substance	5.1	2
Sodium phenolate, solid	2497	2X	Corrosive substance	8	3

Sodium sulphide, hydrated *with at least 30 percent water of crystallisation*	1849	2X	Corrosive substance	8	2
Stannic chloride, anhydrous	1827	4WE	Corrosive substance	8	2
Stannic chloride pentahydrate	2440	2X	Corrosive substance	8	3
Strontium arsenite	1691	2X	Toxic substance	6.1	2
Strontium chlorate, solution	1506	1SE	Oxidising substance	5.1	2
Strontium perchlorate, solution	1508	1Y	Oxidising substance	5.1	2
Strychnine *or* Strychnine salts	1692	2X	Toxic substance	6.1	1
Styrene monomer, inhibited	2055	3 Y	Flammable liquid	3	2
Sulphur	1350	2 Z	Flammable solid	4.1	3
Sulphur chlorides	1828	2RE	Corrosive substance	8	1
Sulphur dichloride	See Sulphur chlorides				—
Sulphur dioxide, liquefied	1079	2RE	Toxic gas	2	—
Sulphur hexafluoride	1080	2RE	Non-flammable compressed gas	2	—
Sulphuretted hydrogen	See Hydrogen sulphide				—
Sulphur, molten	2448	2X	Flammable solid	4.1	3
Sulphuric acid	1830	2P	Corrosive substance	8	2
Sulphuric acid, fuming	1831	4WE	Corrosive substance	8	1

119

Name of Substance 1	Substance Identification No. 2	Emergency Action Code 3	Classification for Conveyance 4	UN Class 5	Packing Group 6
Sulphuric acid, spent	1832	2P	Corrosive substance	8	★
Sulphur monochloride	See Sulphur chlorides				—
Sulphurous acid	1833	2R	Corrosive substance	8	2
Sulphur trioxide, inhibited	1829	4WE	Corrosive substance	8	1
Sulphuryl chloride	1834	4WE	Corrosive substance	8	1
Tars, liquid *including road asphalt and oils, bitumen and cut backs*	1999	2W	Flammable liquid	3	★
Tartar emetic	See Antimony potassium tartrate				—
Terpinolene	2541	3Y	Flammable liquid	3	3
Tetrabromoethane	2504	2Z	Harmful substance	6.1	3
Tetrachloroethane	1702	2XE	Toxic substance	6.1	2
Tetrachloroethylene	1897	2Z	Harmful substance	6.1	3
Tetraethylenepentamine	2320	2R	Corrosive substance	8	3
Tetraethyl lead	See Motor fuel anti-knock mixtures				—
Tetraethyl silicate	1292	3Y	Flammable liquid	3	2
Tetrafluorodichloroethane	See Dichlorotetrafluoroethane				—
1, 2, 3, 6-Tetrahydrobenzaldehyde	2498	3Y	Flammable liquid	3	3

* Check with consignor

Tetrahydrofuran	2056	2SE	Flammable liquid	3	2
Tetrahydro-1, 4-oxazine	See Morpholine				
Tetrahydrophthalic anhydrides	2698	2Z	Corrosive substance	8	3
1, 2, 5, 6-Tetrahydropyridine	2410	2WE	Flammable liquid	3	2
Tetrahydrothiophene	2412	3WE	Flammable liquid	3	2
Tetramethoxysilane	See Methyl orthosilicate				
Tetramethylammonium hydroxide	1835	2R	Corrosive substance	8	2
Tetramethylene cyanide	See Adiponitrile				
Tetramethyl lead	See Motor fuel anti-knock mixtures				
Tetramethylsilane	2749	3WE	Flammable liquid	3	1
Tetranitromethane	1510	2WE	Oxidising substance	5.1	1
Tetrapropyl orthotitanate	2413	2YE	Flammable liquid	3	2
Thioacetic acid	2436	2PE	Flammable liquid	3	2
Thiocarbamide	See Thiourea				
Thioglycolic acid	1940	2X	Corrosive substance	8	2
Thionyl chloride	1836	4WE	Corrosive substance	8	1
Thiophene	2414	3WE	Flammable liquid	3	2
Thiophenol	See Phenyl mercaptan				
Thiophosgene	2474	2XE	Toxic substance	6.1	2

Name of Substance 1	Substance Identification No. 2	Emergency Action Code 3	Classification for Conveyance 4	UN Class 5	Packing Group 6
Thiophosphoryl chloride	1837	4XE	Corrosive substance	8	2
Thiourea	2877	1 Z	Harmful substance	6.1	3
Tin tetrachloride	See Stannic chloride, anhydrous			—	—
Titanium tetrachloride	1838	4WE	Corrosive substance	8	2
Toluene	1294	3 Y E	Flammable liquid	3	2
Toluene di-isocyanate	2078	2XE	Toxic substance	6.1	2
Toluene sulphonic acids, liquid	See the three entries for Alkyl or Aryl sulphonic acids, liquid			—	—
Toluidines	1708	3X	Toxic substance	6.1	2
Toluol	See Toluene			—	—
2, 4-Toluylenediamine	1709	2X	Harmful substance	6.1	3
Toluylene di-isocyanate	See Toluene di-isocyanate			—	—
Tolylene di-isocyanate	See Toluene di-isocyanate			—	—
Tolyethylene	See Vinyl toluene			—	—
Triallylamine	2610	3Y	Flammable liquid	3	2
Tri-(1-aziridinyl) phosphine oxide, solution	2510	2X	Toxic substance	6.1	★
Tribromoborane	See Boron tribromide			—	—

* Check with consignor

Tributylamine	2542	3X	Corrosive substance	8	3
Trichloroacetaldehyde	See Chloral				
Trichloroacetic acid, solution	2564	2R	Corrosive substance	8	2
Trichloroaceticaldeheyde	See Chloral				
Trichloroacetyl chloride	2442	2R	Corrosive substance	8	2
Trichlorobenzenes, liquid	2321	2Z	Harmful substance	6.1	3
Trichlorobutene	2322	2Z	Toxic substance	6.1	3
1, 1, 1-Trichloroethane	2831	2 Z	Harmful substance	6.1	3
Trichloroethylene	1710	2Z	Harmful substance	6.1	3
Trichloronitromethane	See Chloropicrin				
Trichlorosilane	1295	4WE	Substance which in contact with water emits flammable gas	4.3	1
2, 4 6-Trichloro-1, 3, 5-triazine	See Cyanuric chloride				
Tricresylphosphate *with more than 3 percent ortho isomer*	2574	2X	Toxic substance	6.1	2
Triethyl aluminium	See Aluminium alkyls				
Triethylamine	1296	3WE	Flammable liquid	3	2
Triethyl borate	See Ethyl borate				
Triethylene tetramine	2259	2R	Corrosive substance	8	2

Name of Substance 1	Substance Identification No. 2	Emergency Action Code 3	Classification for Conveyance 4	UN Class 5	Packing Group 6
Triethyl orthoformate	See Ethyl orthoformate				
Triethyl phosphite	2323	3Y	Flammable liquid	3	3
Trifluoroacetic acid	2699	2X	Corrosive substance	8	1
Trifluorobromomethane	See Bromotrifluoromethane				
Trifluorochloroethane	See Chlorotrifluoroethane				
Trifluorochloroethylene, inhibited	1082	2WE	Flammable gas	2	—
Trifluoroethane, compressed	2035	2WE	Flammable gas	2	—
Trifluoromethane	1984	2RE	Non-flammable compressed gas	2	—
Trifluoromethane and Chlorotri-fluoromethane azeotropic mixture	See Chlorotrifluoromethane and Trifluoromethane azeotropic mixture				
Triisobutyl aluminium	See Aluminium alkyls				
Triisobutylene	2324	3 Y	Flammable liquid	3	2
Triisopropyl borate	2616	2 S	Flammable liquid	3	2
Trimethyl acetyl chloride	2438	4WE	Corrosive substance	8	2
Trimethyl aluminium	See Aluminium alkyls				
Trimethylamine, anhydrous	1083	2PE	Flammable gas	2	—

Trimethylamine, aqueous solutions not more than 50 percent of trimethylamine, by weight	1297	2PE	Flammable liquid	3	★
1, 3, 5-Trimethylbenzene	2325	3 Y	Flammable liquid	3	3
Trimethyl borate	2416	2 S	Flammable liquid	3	2
Trimethylchlorosilane	1298	4WE	Flammable liquid	3	1
Trimethylcyclohexylamine	2326	3X	Corrosive substance	8	3
Trimethylene chlorobromide	See 1-Chloro-3-bromopropane				—
Trimethylhexamethylenediamines	2327	2R	Corrosive substance	8	3
Trimethylhexamethylenediisocyanate	2328	3X	Harmful substance	6.1	3
2, 4, 4-Trimethyl pentene-1	See Diisobutylene				—
2, 4, 4-Trimethyl pentene-2	See Diisobutylene				—
Trimethyl phosphite	2329	3Y	Flammable liquid	3	3
Tripropyl aluminium	See Aluminium alkyls				—
Tripropylamine	2260	3W	Flammable liquid	3	2
Tripropylene	2057	3 Y	Flammable liquid	3	2
Tropilidene	See Cycloheptatriene				—
Turpentine	1299	3 Y	Flammable liquid	3	3
Turpentine substitute	1300	3 Y	Flammable liquid	3	★
Valeral	See Valeraldehyde				—

* Check with consignor

Name of Substance 1	Substance Identification No. 2	Emergency Action Code 3	Classification for Conveyance 4	UN Class 5	Packing Group 6
Valeraldehyde	2058	3 Y E	Flammable liquid	3	2
n-Valeraldehyde	See Valeraldehyde				
Valeric aldehyde	See Valeraldehyde				
Valeryl chloride	2502	3WE	Corrosive substance	8	2
Vanadium oxytrichloride	2443	2X	Corrosive substance	8	2
Vanadium pentoxide, *non-fused form*	2862	1Z	Toxic substance	6.1	2
Vanadium tetrachloride	2444	4WE	Corrosive substance	8	1
Vanadium trichloride	2475	2X	Corrosive substance	8	3
Vanadium trioxide, *non-fused form*	2860	1Z	Toxic substance	6.1	2
Villiaumite	See Sodium fluoride				
Vinyl acetate, inhibited	1301	3 Y E	Flammable liquid	3	2
Vinylbenzene	See Styrene monomer				
Vinyl bromide, inhibited	1085	3YE	Toxic gas	2	
Vinyl butyrate, inhibited	2838	3 Y E	Flammable liquid	3	2
Vinyl chloride, inhibited	1086	2WE	Flammable gas	2	
Vinyl chloroacetate	2589	2XE	Toxic substance	6.1	2
Vinyl ethyl ether, inhibited	1302	3YE	Flammable liquid	3	1

Vinyl fluoride, inhibited	1860	2WE	Flammable gas	2	—
Vinylidene chloride, inhibited	1303	3YE	Flammable liquid	3	1
Vinyl isobutyl ether, inhibited	1304	3YE	Flammable liquid	3	2
Vinyl methyl ether, inhibited	1087	2WE	Flammable gas	2	—
Vinyl toluene, inhibited	2618	3 Y	Flammable liquid	3	3
Vinyltrichlorosilane, inhibited	1305	4WE	Flammable liquid	3	1
White arsenic	See Arsenic trioxide				
White spirit	See Turpentine substitute				
Xylenes	1307	3 Y	Flammable liquid	3	★
Xylenols	2261	2X	Toxic substance	6.1	2
Xylidines	1711	3X	Toxic substance	6.1	2
Xylols	See Xylenes				
Xylyl bromide	1701	2XE	Toxic substance	6.1	2
Zinc arsenate, Zinc arsenite or Zinc arsenate and Zinc arsenite mixtures	1712	2Z	Toxic substance	6.1	2
Zinc chlorate, solution	1513	1YE	Oxidising substance	5.1	2
Zinc chloride, solution	1840	2X	Corrosive substance	8	3
Zinc fluorosilicate	2855	1Z	Harmful substance	6.1	3
Zinc silicofluoride	See Zinc fluorosilicate				
Zirconium tetrachloride	2503	4WE	Corrosive substance	8	3

* Check with consignor

LIST OF DANGEROUS SUBSTANCES (Alphabetical)

PART 2 MIXTURES AND OTHER SUBSTANCES NOT SPECIFIED IN PART 1

In this part 'NOS' means 'not specified in Part 1 of the Approved List'

Name of Substance 1	Substance Identification No. 2	Emergency Action Code 3	Classification for Conveyance 4	UN Class 5	Packing Group 6
Alkylamines, NOS *or* Polyalkylamines, NOS *corrosive*	2735	3W	Corrosive substance	8	★
Alkylamines, NOS *or* Polyalkylamines, NOS *corrosive, flammable, flash point 21°C or above*	2734	3W	Corrosive substance	8	★
Alkylamines, NOS *or* Polyalkylamines, NOS *flammable, corrosive, flash point less than 21°C*	2733	3WE	Flammable liquid	8	★
Barium compounds, NOS *except Barium sulphate*	1564	2Z	Toxic substance	6.1	★
Bifluorides, NOS	1740	2X	Corrosive substance	8	2
Bisulphites, inorganic, aqueous solutions, NOS	2693	2R	Corrosive substance	8	3
Caustic alkali liquids, NOS *miscible with water, non-toxic*	1719	2R	Corrosive substance	8	2

* Check with consignor

Chlorates, inorganic, solution, NOS *except ammonium chlorate*	1461	2YE	Oxidising substance	5.1	2
Chlorites, inorganic, solution, NOS	1462	2PE	Oxidising substance	5.1	2
Corrosive liquid, harmful, mixture, NOS *immiscible with water*	2922	3X	Corrosive substance	8	★
Corrosive liquid, harmful, mixture, NOS *miscible with water*	2922	2X	Corrosive substance	8	★
Corrosive liquid, harmful, mixture, NOS *reacts violently with water*	2922	4WE	Corrosive substance	8	★
Corrosive liquid, mixture, NOS *immiscible with water*	1760	3X	Corrosive substance	8	★
Corrosive liquid, mixture, NOS *miscible with water*	1760	2R	Corrosive substance	8	★
Corrosive liquid, mixture, NOS *reacts violently with water*	1760	4WE	Corrosive substance	8	★
Corrosive liquid, toxic, mixture, NOS *immiscible with water*	2922	3XE	Corrosive substance	8	★
Corrosive liquid, toxic, mixture, NOS *miscible with water*	2922	2XE	Corrosive substance	8	★
Corrosive liquid, toxic, mixture, NOS *reacts violently with water*	2922	4WE	Corrosive substance	8	★
Corrosive solid, mixture, NOS	1759	2X	Corrosive substance	8	★

* Check with consignor

Name of Substance 1	Substance Identification No. 2	Emergency Action Code 3	Classification for Conveyance 4	UN Class 5	Packing Group 6
Corrosive solid, mixture, NOS *reacts violently with water*	1759	4WE	Corrosive substance	8	★
Flammable liquid, corrosive, mixture, NOS *immiscible with water, flash point 21°C or above*	2924	3W	Flammable liquid	3	★
Flammable liquid, corrosive, mixture, NOS *miscible with water, flash point 21°C or above*	2924	2W	Flammable liquid	3	★
Flammable liquid, corrosive, mixture, NOS *immiscible with water, flash point less than 21°C*	2924	3WE	Flammable liquid	3	★
Flammable liquid, corrosive, mixture, NOS *miscible with water, flash point less than 21°c*	2924	2WE	Flammable liquid	3	★
Flammable liquid, corrosive, mixture, NOS *reacts violently with water*	2924	4WE	Flammable liquid	3	★
Flammable liquid, harmful, mixture, NOS *immiscible with water, flash point 21°C or above*	1992	3 Y	Flammable liquid	3	★

* Check with consignor

Flammable liquid, harmful, mixture, NOS *miscible with water, flash point 21°C or above*	1992	2 Y	Flammable liquid	3	★
Flammable liquid, harmful, mixture, NOS *immiscible with water, flash point less than 21°C*	1992	3 Y E	Flammable liquid	3	★
Flammable liquid, harmful, mixture, NOS *miscible with water, flash point less than 21°C*	1992	2 Y E	Flammable liquid	3	★
Flammable liquid, mixture NOS *immiscible with water, flash point 21°C or above*	1993	3 Y	Flammable liquid	3	★
Flammable liquid, mixture, NOS *miscible with water, flash point 21°C or above*	1993	2 Y	Flammable liquid	3	★
Flammable liquid, mixture, NOS *immiscible with water, flash point less than 21°C*	1993	3 Y E	Flammable liquid	3	★
Flammable liquid, mixture, NOS *miscible with water, flash point less than 21°C*	1993	2 Y E	Flammable liquid	3	★
Flammable liquid, toxic, mixture, NOS *immiscible with water*	1992	3WE	Flammable liquid	3	★
Flammable liquid, toxic, mixture, NOS *miscible with water*	1992	2WE	Flammable liquid	3	★

* Check with consignor

Name of Substance 1	Substance Identification No. 2	Emergency Action Code 3	Classification for Conveyance 4	UN Class 5	Packing Group 6
Flammable solid, corrosive, mixture, NOS	2925	2W	Flammable solid	3	★
Flammable solid, corrosive, mixture, NOS *reacts violently with water*	2925	4WE	Flammable solid	3	★
Flammable solid, harmful, mixture, NOS	2926	2 Y	Flammable solid	3	★
Flammable solid, mixture, NOS	1325	2 Y	Flammable solid	3	★
Flammable solid, toxic, mixture, NOS	2926	2WE	Flammable solid	3	★
Harmful liquid, mixture, NOS *immiscible with water*	2810	3 Z	Harmful substance	6.1	★
Harmful liquid, mixture, NOS *miscible with water*	2810	2 Z	Harmful substance	6.1	★
Harmful solid, mixture, NOS	2811	2 Z	Harmful substance	6.1	★
Hazardous waste, containing isocyanates, NOS	7022	4WE	Other dangerous substance	9	★
Hazardous waste, containing organo-lead compounds, NOS	7023	4WE	Other dangerous subtance	9	★
Hazardous waste, flammable, solid or sludge, NOS	7012	3WE	Other dangerous substance	9	★

* Check with consignor

Substance	UN No.	Code	Description		Class	
Hazardous waste, liquid, agrochemicals, toxic, NOS	7021	4WE	Other dangerous substance		9	★
Hazardous waste, liquid, NOS	7015	2X	Other dangerous substance		9	★
Hazardous waste, liquid, toxic, NOS	7017	2X	Other dangerous substance		9	★
Hazardous waste, solid or sludge, agrochemicals, toxic, NOS	7020	4WE	Other dangerous substance		9	★
Hazardous waste, solid or sludge, NOS	7014	2X	Other dangerous substance		9	★
Hazardous waste, solid or sludge, toxic, NOS	7016	2X	Other dangerous substance		9	★
Hydrocarbon gases, liquefied, NOS or Hydrocarbon gases mixtures, liquefied, NOS	1965	2WE	Flammable gas		2	★
Isocyanates, NOS or Isocyanate solutions, NOS *flash point less than 21 °C*	2478	3WE	Flammable liquid		3	★
Lead compounds, soluble, NOS	2291	2Z	Harmful substance		6.1	3
Organochlorine pesticides, liquid, harmful, NOS *miscible with water*	2996	2X	Harmful substance		6.1	★
Organochlorine pesticides, liquid, harmful, NOS *immiscible with water*	2996	3X	Harmful substance		6.1	★

* Check with consignor

Name of Substance 1	Substance Identification No. 2	Emergency Action Code 3	Classification for Conveyance 4	UN Class 5	Packing Group 6
Perchlorates, inorganic, solution, NOS *except ammonium perchlorate*	1481	2WE	Oxidising substance	5.1	2
Petroleum distillates, NOS *Benzene content less than 5 percent, flash point less than 21°C*	1268	3 Y E	Flammable liquid	3	★
Petroleum distillates, NOS *Benzene content less than 5 percent, flash point 21°C or above*	1268	3 Y	Flammable liquid	3	★
Petroleum fuel, NOS *flash point less than 21°C*	1270	3 Y E	Flammable liquid	3	★
Petroleum fuel, NOS *flash point 21°C or above*	1270	3 Y	Flammable liquid	3	★
Phenylmercuric compounds, NOS	2026	2X	Toxic substance	6.1	★
Resin solutions in flammable liquids, toxic, NOS				3	★
Miscible with water, flash point less than 21°C	1866	2WE	Flammable liquid		
Miscible with water, flash point 21°C or above	1866	2W	Flammable liquid		
Immiscible with water, flash point less than 21°C	1866	3WE	Flammable liquid		

★ Check with consignor

Immiscible with water, flash point 21°C or above	1866	Flammable liquid	3W	3	★
Resin solutions in flammable liquids, non-toxic, NOS					
Miscible with water, flash point less than 21°C	1866	Flammable liquid	2 Y E		
Miscible with water, flash point 21°C or above	1866	Flammable liquid	2 Y		
Immiscible with water, flash point less than 21°C	1866	Flammable liquid	3 Y E		
Immiscible with water, flash point 21°C or above	1866	Flammable liquid	3 Y		
Terpene hydrocarbons, NOS	2319	Flammable liquid	3 Y	3	★
Toxic liquid, corrosive, mixture, NOS *immiscible with water*	2927	Toxic substance	3XE	6.1	★
Toxic liquid, corrosive, mixture, NOS *miscible with water*	2927	Toxic substance	2XE	6.1	★
Toxic liquid, corrosive, mixture, NOS *reacts violently with water*	2927	Toxic substance	4WE	6.1	★
Toxic liquid, flammable, mixture, NOS *immiscible with water*	2929	Toxic substance	3WE	6.1	★
Toxic liquid, flammable, mixture, NOS *miscible with water*	2929	Toxic substance	2WE	6.1	★
Toxic liquid, mixture, NOS *immiscible with water*	2810	Toxic substance	3XE	6.1	★

* Check with consignor

Name of Substance 1	Substance Identification No. 2	Emergency Action Code 3	Classification for Conveyance 4	UN Class 5	Packing Group 6
Toxic liquid, mixture, NOS *miscible with water*	2810	2XE	Toxic substance	6.1	★
Toxic solid, corrosive, mixture, NOS	2928	2XE	Toxic substance	6.1	★
Toxic solid, corrosive, mixture, NOS *reacts violently with water*	2928	4WE	Toxic substance	6.1	★
Toxic solid, flammable, mixture, NOS	2930	2WE	Toxic substance	6.1	★
Toxic solid, mixture, NOS	2811	2XE	Toxic substance	6.1	★

* Check with consignor

136

LIST OF DANGEROUS SUBSTANCES (Alphabetical)

PART 3 GROUPS OF SUBSTANCES NOT LISTED IN PARTS 1 AND 2

Name of Substance	Substance Identification No.	Emergency Action Code	Classification for Conveyance	UN Class	Packing Group
1	2	3	4	5	6
Antimony compounds, inorganic, nos including sulphides and oxides with more than 0.5% arsenic	1549	—	Toxic substance	6.1	1 or 2
Antimony compounds, inorganic, nos including sulphides and oxides with more than 0.5% arsenic	1549	—	Harmful substance	6.1	3
Arsenical pesticides, liquid, flammable, toxic, nos, *flash point less than 21°C*	2760	—	Flammable liquid	3	1 or 2
Arsenical pesticides, liquid flammable, harmful, nos, *flash point less than 21°C*	2760	—	Flammable liquid	3	1 or 2
Arsenical pesticides, liquid, toxic, flammable, nos, *flash point not less than 21°C*	2993	—	Toxic substance	6.1	1 or 2
Arsenical pesticides, liquid, harmful, flammable, nos, *flash point not less than 21°C*	2993	—	Flammable liquid	3	3
Arsenical pesticides, liquid, toxic, nos	2994	—	Toxic substance	6.1	1 or 2

Name of Substance 1	Substance Identification No. 2	Emergency Action Code 3	Classification for Conveyance 4	UN Class 5	Packing Group 6
Arsenical pesticides, liquid, harmful, nos	2994	—	Harmful substance	6.1	3
Arsenical pesticides, solid, toxic, nos	2759	—	Toxic substance	6.1	1 or 2
Arsenical pesticides, solid, harmful nos	2759	—	Harmful substance	6.1	3
Arsenic compounds, liquid, nos, including: Arsenates, nos; Arsenites, nos; Arsenic sulphides, nos and Organic compounds of arsenic nos	1556	—	Toxic substance	6.1	3
Arsenic compounds, liquid nos, including Arsenates, nos, Arsenites, nos, Arsenic sulphides, nos and Organic compounds of arsenic nos	1556	—	Harmful substance	6.1	3
Arsenic compounds, solid, nos, including: Arsenates, nos; Arsenites, nos; Arsenic sulphides, nos and Organic compounds of arsenic, nos	1557	—	Toxic substance	6.1	1 or 2
Arsenic compounds, solid, nos, including: Arsenates, nos: Arsenites, nos; Arsenic sulphides, nos and Organic compounds or arsenic, nos	1557	—	Harmful substance	6.1	1 or 2

Name	UN No.		Hazard	Class	
Barium alloys	1399	—	Substance which in contact with water emits flammable gas	4.3	2
Barium alloys, pyrophoric	1854	—	Spontaneously combustible substance	4.2	2
Barium compounds, nos	1564	—	Toxic substance	6.1	3
Barium compounds, nos	1564	—	Harmful substance	6.1	3
Battery fluid, acid	2796	—	Corrosive substance	8	2
Battery fluid, alkali	2797	2R	Corrosive substance	8	2
Benzoic derivative pesticides, liquid, flammable, toxic, nos, *flash point less than 21°C*	2770	—	Flammable liquid	3	1 or 2
Benzoic derivative pesticides, liquid, flammable, harmful nos, *flash point less than 21°C*	2770	—	Flammable liquid	3	1 or 2
Benzoic derivative pesticides, liquid, flammable, toxic, nos, *flash point not less than 21°C*	3003	—	Toxic substance	6.1	1 or 2
Benzoic derivative pesticides, liquid, flammable, harmful nos, *flash point not less than 21°C*	3003	—	Flammable liquid	3	3
Benzoic derivative pesticides, liquid, toxic nos	3004	—	Toxic substance	6.1	1 or 2

Name of Substance 1	Substance Identification No. 2	Emergency Action Code 3	Classification for Conveyance 4	UN Class 5	Packing Group 6
Benzoic derivative pesticides, liquid, harmful nos	3004	—	Harmful substance	6.1	3
Benzoic derivative pesticides, solid, toxic, nos	2769	—	Toxic substance	6.1	1 or 2
Benzoic derivative pesticides, solid, harmful nos	2769	—	Harmful substance	6.1	3
Beryllium compounds, nos	1566	—	Toxic substance	6.1	2
Bifluorides, nos	1740	—	Corrosive substance	8	2
Bipyridilium pesticides liquid, flammable, toxic, nos *flash point less than 21°C*	2782	—	Flammable liquid	3	1 or 2
Bipyridilium pesticides liquid, flammable, harmful, nos, *flash point less than 21°C*	2782	—	Flammable liquid	3	1 or 2
Bipyridilium pesticides, liquid, toxic, flammable, harmful, *flash point not 21°C*	3015	—	Toxic substance	6.1	3
Bipyridilium pesticides, liquid, flammable, harmful, *flash point not less than 21°C*	3015	—	Flammable liquid	3	3

Bipyridilium pesticides, liquid, toxic nos	3016	—	Toxic substance	6.1	1 or 2
Bipyridilium pesticides, liquid, harmful, nos	3016	—	Harmful substance	6.1	3
Bipyridilium pesticides, solid, toxic, nos	2781	—	Toxic substance	6.1	1 or 2
Bipyridilium pesticides, solid, harmful, nos	2781	—	Harmful substance	6.1	3
Bisulphites, inorganic, aqueous solutions of, nos	2693	—	Corrosive substance	8	3
Cadmium compounds, nos	2570	—	Toxic substance	6.1	1 or 2
Cadmium compounds, nos	2570	—	Harmful substance	6.1	3
Calcium or Calcium alloys	1401	—	Substance which in contact with water emits flammable gas 4.3	4.3	3
Calcium alloys, pyrophoric	1855	—	Spontaneously combustible substance	4.2	2
Carbamate pesticides, liquid, flammable, toxic, nos, *flash point less than 21°C*	2758	—	Flammable liquid	3	1 or 2

LIST OF DANGEROUS SUBSTANCES (Alphabetical)

PART 3 GROUPS OF SUBSTANCES NOT LISTED IN PARTS 1 AND 2

Name of Substance 1	Substance Identification No. 2	Emergency Action Code 3	Classification for Conveyance 4	UN Class 5	Packing Group 6
Carbamate pesticides, liquid, flammable, harmful, nos, *flash point less than 21°C*	2758	—	Flammable liquid	3	1 or 2
Carbamate pesticides, liquid, toxic, flammable, nos, *flash point not less than 21°C*	2991	—	Toxic substance	6.1	1 or 2
Carbamate pesticides, liquid, flammable, harmful, nos, *flash point not less than 21°C*	2991	—	Flammable liquid	3	3
Carbamate pesticides, liquid, toxic, nos	2992	—	Toxic substance	6.1	1 or 2
Carbamate pesticides liquid, harmful, nos	2992	—	Harmful substance	6.1	3
Carbamate pesticides, solid, toxic, nos	2757	—	Toxic substance	6.1	1 or 2
Carbamate pesticides, solid, harmful, nos	2757	—	Harmful substance	6.1	3
Caustic alkali liquids, nos	1719	—	Corrosive substance	8	2

Chlorate and borate mixtures	1458	—	Oxidising substance	5.1	2
Chlorites, inorganic, nos	1462	—	Oxidising substance	5.1	2
Chloroformates, nos, *flash point not less than 21°C*	2742	—	Toxic substance	6.1	2
Chloropicrin mixtures, nos	1583	—	Toxic subtance	6.1	1 or 2
Chloropicrin mixtures, nos	1583	—	Harmful substance	6.1	3
Chlorosilanes, nos	2987	—	Corrosive substance	8	2
Chlorosilanes, nos, *flash point not less than 21°C*	2985	—	Flammable liquid	3	1
Chlorosilanes, nos, *flash point not less than 21°C*	2986	—	Corrosive substance	8	2
Chlorosilanes, nos, *which in contact with water emit flammable gases*	2988	—	Substance which in contact with water emits flammable gas	4.3	1
Compressed *or* liquefied gases, flammable, nos	1954	—	Flammable gas	2	—
Compressed *or* liquefied gases, flammable, toxic, nos	1953	—	Toxic gas	2	—
Compressed *or* liquefied gases, nos	1956	—	Non-flammable compressed gas	2	—
Compressed *or* liquefied gases, toxic, nos	1955	—	Toxic gas	2	—

Name of Substance 1	Substance Identification No. 2	Emergency Action Code 3	Classification for Conveyance 4	UN Class 5	Packing Group 6
Copper based pesticides liquid, flammable, toxic, nos, *flash point not less than 21°C*	2776	—	Flammable liquid	3	1 or 2
Copper based pesticides liquid, flammable, harmful, nos, *flash point not less than 21°C*	2776	—	Flammable liquid	3	1 or 2
Copper based pesticides, liquid, toxic, flammable, nos, *flash point not less than 21°C*	3009	—	Toxic substance	6.1	1 or 2
Copper based pesticides, liquid, flammable, harmful, nos, *flash point not less than 21°C*	3009	—	Flammable liquid	3	3
Copper based pesticides, liquid, toxic, nos	3010	—	Toxic substance	6.1	1 or 2
Copper based pesticides, liquid, harmful, nos	3010	—	Harmful substance	6.1	3
Copper based pesticides, solid, toxic nos	2775	—	Toxic substance	6.1	1 or 2
Copper based pesticides, solid, harmful, nos	2775	—	Harmful substance	6.1	3
Corrosive liquids, flammable, nos	2920	—	Corrosive substance	8	1 or 2

Corrosive liquids nos	1760	—	Corrosive substance	8	—
Corrosive liquids, toxic, nos	2922	—	Corrosive substance	8	1 or 2
Corrosives liquids, harmful, nos	2922	—	Corrosive substance	8	*
Corrosive solids, flammable, nos	2921	—	Corrosive substance	8	*
Corrosive solids, nos	1759	—	Corrosive substance	8	*
Corrosive solids, toxic, nos	2923	—	Corrosive substance	8	1 or 2
Corrosive solids, harmful, nos	2923	—	Corrosive substance	8	—
Coumarin derivative pesticides, liquid, flammable, toxic, nos, *flash point less than 21°C*	3024	—	Flammable liquid	3	1 or 2
Coumarin derivative pesticides, liquid, flammable, harmful, nos, *flash point less than 21°C*	3024	—	Flammable liquid	3	1 or 2
Coumarin derivative pesticides, liquid, toxic, flammable, nos, *flash point not less than 21°C*	3025	—	Toxic substance	6.1	1 or 2
Coumarin derivative pesticides, liquid, flammable, harmful, nos, *flash point not less than 21°C*	3025	—	Flammable liquid	3	3
Coumarin derivative pesticides, liquid, toxic, nos	3026	—	Toxic substance	6.1	1 or 2
Coumarin derivative pesticides, liquid harmful, nos	3026	—	Harmful substance	6.1	3

* Check with consignor

Name of Substance 1	Substance Identification No. 2	Emergency Action Code 3	Classification for Conveyance 4	UN Class 5	Packing Group 6
Coumarin derivative pesticides, solid, toxic nos	3027	—	Toxic substance	6.1	1 or 2
Coumarin derivative pesticides, solid, harmful, nos	3027	—	Harmful substance	6.1	3
Cyanides, inorganic, nos, *except ferricyanides and ferrocyanides*	1588	—	Toxic substance	6.1	1 or 2
Cyanides, inorganic, nos, *except ferricyanides and ferrocyanides*	1588	—	Harmful substance	6.1	3
Cyanide solutions	1935	—	Toxic substance	6.1	1
Disinfectants, nos, toxic	1601	—	Toxic substance	6.1	1 or 2

*Check with consignor

LIST OF DANGEROUS SUBSTANCES (Alphabetical)

PART 3 GROUPS OF SUBSTANCES NOT LISTED IN PARTS 1 AND 2

Name of Substance 1	Substance Identification No. 2	Emergency Action Code 3	Classification for Conveyance 4	UN Class 5	Packing Group 6
Disinfectants, nos, harmful	1601	—	Harmful substance	6.1	3
Dithiocarbamate pesticides, liquid, flammable, toxic, nos, *flash point less than 21°C*	2772	—	Flammable liquid	3	*
Dithiocarbamate pesticide liquid, flammable, harmful, nos, *flash point less than 21°C*	2772	—	Flammable liquid	3	1 or 2
Dithiocarbamate pesticides, liquid, toxic, flammable, nos, *flash point not less than 21°C*	3005	—	Toxic substance	6.1	1 or 2
Dithiocarbamate pesticides liquid, harmful, flammable, nos, *flash point not less than 21°C*	3005	—	Flammable liquid	3	3
Dithiocarbamate pesticides, liquid, toxic, nos	3006	—	Toxic substance	6.1	1 or 2
Dithiocarbamate pesticides, liquid, harmful, nos	3006	—	Harmful substance	6.1	3
Dithiocarbamate pesticides, solid, toxic, nos	2771	—	Toxic substance	6.1	1 or 2

* Check with consignor

Name of Substance 1	Substance Identification No. 2	Emergency Action Code 3	Classification for Conveyance 4	UN Class 5	Packing Group 6
Dithiocarbamate pesticides solid, harmful, nos	2771	—	Harmful substance	6.1	3
Dyes, nos *or* Dye intermediates, nos	1602	—	Toxic substance	6.1	1 or 2
Dyes, nos *or* Dye intermediates, nos	1602	—	Harmful substance	6.1	3
Fire extinguisher charges, *corrosive liquid*	1774	—	Corrosive substance	8	2
Flammable liquids, corrosive, nos	2924	—	Flammable liquid	3	*
Flammable liquids, nos	1993	—	Flammable liquid	3	*
Flammable liquids, toxic nos	1992	—	Flammable liquid	3	1 or 2
Flammable liquids, harmful, nos	1992	—	Flammable liquid	3	*
Flammable solids, corrosive nos	2925	—	Flammable solid	4.1	*
Flammable solids, nos	1325	—	Flammable solid	4.1	2
Flammable solids, toxic nos	2926	—	Flammable solid	4.1	—
Fluorosilicates, nos	2856	—	Harmful substance	6.1	3
Fuel, pyrophoric, nos	1375	—	Spontaneously combustible substance	4.2	1
Halogenated irritating liquids, toxic, nos	1610	—	Toxic substance	6.1	1 or 2

* Check with consignor

Halogenated irritating liquids,	1610	—	Harmful substance	6.1	3
Harmful liquids, nos	2810	—	Harmful substance	6.1	3
Harmful solids, nos	2811	—	Harmful substance	6.1	3
Hydrides, metal, nos	1409	—	Substance which in contact with water emits flammable gas	4.3	1
Hydrocarbon gases, compressed, nos, *or* Hydrocarbon gases mixtures, compressed, nos	1964	—	Flammable gas	2	—
Hydrocarbon gases, liquefied nos, *or* Hydrocarbon gases mixtures, liquefied, nos	1965	—	Flammable gas	2	—
Insecticide gases, nos	1968	—	Non-flammable compressed gas	2	—
Insecticide gases, toxic, nos	1967	—	Toxic gas	2	—
Isocyanates, nos *or* Isocyanate solutions, nos, *boiling point not less than 300°C*	2207	—	Harmful substance	6.1	3
Isocyanates, nos *or* Isocyanate solutions, nos *flash point less than 21°C*	2478	—	Flammable liquid	3	2
Isocyanates, nos *or* Isocyanate solutions, nos, *flash point not less*	2206	—	Toxic substance	6.1	2

Name of Substance 1	Substance Identification No. 2	Emergency Action Code 3	Classification for Conveyance 4	UN Class 5	Packing Group 6
than 21°C and boiling point less than 300°C					
Lead compounds, soluble, nos	2291	—	Harmful substance	6.1	3
Liquefied gases, *charged with nitrogen, carbon dioxide or air*	1058	—	Non-flammable compressed2 gas		—
Lithium alkyls	2445	—	Spontaneously combustible substance	4.2	1
Magnesium alkyls	3053	—	Spontaneously combustible substance	4.2	1
Magnesium alloys, powder	1418	—	Substance which in contact with water emits flammable gas	4.3	2
Magnesium alloys, *with more than 50% magnesium in pellets, turnings or ribbons*	1869	—	Flammable solid	4.1	3
Mercaptans, liquid, nos *or* Mercaptan mixtures liquid, nos	1228	—	Flammable liquid	3	2
Mercaptans, liquid, nos *or* Mercaptan mixtures, liquid, nos, *flash point not less than 21°C*	3071	—	Flammable liquid	3	2

Mercury based pesticides, liquid, flammable, toxic, nos, *flash point less than 21°C*	2778	—	Flammable liquid	3	1 or 2
Mercury based pesticides, liquid, flammable, harmful, nos, *flash point less than 21°C*	2778	—	Flammable liquid	3	1 or 2
Mercury based pesticides, liquid, toxic, flammable, nos, *flash point not less than 21°C*	3011	—	Toxic substance	6.1	1 or 2
Mercury based pesticides, liquid, flammable, harmful, *flash point not less than 21°C*	3011	—	Flammable liquid	3	3
Mercury based pesticides, liquid, toxic, nos	3012	—	Toxic substance	6.1	1 or 2
Mercury based pesticides, liquid, harmful, nos	3012	—	Harmful substance	6.1	3

LIST OF DANGEROUS SUBSTANCES (Alphabetical)

PART 3 GROUPS OF SUBSTANCES NOT LISTED IN PARTS 1 AND 2

Name of Substance 1	Substance Identification No. 2	Emergency Action Code 3	Classification for Conveyance 4	UN Class 5	Packing Group 6
Mercury based pesticides, solid, toxic, nos	2777	—	Toxic substance	6.1	1 or 2
Mercury based pesticides, solid, harmful, nos	2777	—	Harmful substance	6.1	3
Mercury compounds, liquid, nos, *except mercurous chloride and cinnabar*	2024	—	Toxic substance	6.1	1 or 2
Mercury compounds, liquid, nos, *except mercurous chloride and cinnabar*	2024	—	Harmful substance	6.1	3
Mercury compounds, solid, nos, *except mercurous chloride and cinnabar*	2025	—	Toxic substance	6.1	1 or 2
Mercury compounds, solid, nos *except mercurous chloride and cinnabar*	2025	—	Harmful substance	6.1	3
Metal alkyls, nos	2003	—	Spontaneously combustible substance	4.2	1

Metal alkyl halides, nos	3049	—	Spontaneously combustible substance	4.2	1
Metal alkyl hydrides, nos	3050	—	Spontaneously combustible substance	4.2	1
Nicotine compounds, nos *or* Nicotine preparations nos	1655	—	Toxic substance	6.1	1 or 2
Nicotine compounds, nos *or* Nicotine preparations nos	1655	—	Harmful substance	6.1	3
Nitrates, inorganic, nos	1477	—	Oxidising substance	5.1	2
Organochlorine pesticides, liquid, flammable, harmful, nos, *flash point than 21°C*	2762	—	Flammable liquid	3	1 or 2
Organochlorine pesticides, liquid, flammable, harmful, nos, *flash point less than 21°C*	2762	—	Flammable liquid	3	1 or 2
Organochlorine pesticides, liquid, toxic, flammable, nos, *flash point not less than 21°C*	2995	—	Toxic substance	6.1	1 or 2
Organochlorine pesticides, liquid, flammable, harmful, nos, *flash point not less than 21°C*	2995	—	Flammable liquid	3	3
Organochlorine pesticides, liquid, toxic, nos	2996	—	Toxic substance	6.1	1 or 2

Name of Substance 1	Substance Identification No. 2	Emergency Action Code 3	Classification for Conveyance 4	UN Class 5	Packing Group 6
Organochlorine pesticides, liquid, harmful, nos	2996	—	Harmful substance	6.1	3
Organochlorine pesticides, solid, toxic, nos	2761	—	Toxic substance	6.1	1 or 2
Organochlorine pesticides, solid, harmful, nos	2761	—	Harmful substance	6.1	3
Organophosphorus pesticides, liquid, flammable, toxic, nos, *flash point less than 21°C*	2784	—	Flammable liquid	3	1 or 2
Phenyl urea pesticides, liquid, flammable, toxic, nos *flash point less than 21°C*	2768	—	Flammable liquid	3	1 or 2
Phenyl urea pesticides, liquid, flammable, harmful, *flash point less than 21°C*	2768	—	Flammable liquid	3	1 or 2
Phenyl urea pesticides, liquid, toxic, nos *flash point not less than 21°C*	3001	—	Toxic substance	6.1	1 or 2
Phenyl urea pesticides, liquid, flammable, harmful, nos *flash point not less than 21°C*	3001	—	Flammable liquid	3	3

Phenyl urea pesticides, liquid, toxic, nos	3002	—	Toxic substance	6.1	1 or 2
Phenyl urea pesticides, liquid, harmful, nos	3002	—	Harmful substance	6.1	3
Phenyl urea pesticides, solid, toxic, nos	2767	—	Toxic substance	6.1	1 or 2
Phenyl urea pesticides, solid, harmful, nos	2767	—	Harmful substance	6.1	3
Phthalimide derivative pesticides, liquid, flammable, toxic, nos *flash point less than 21°C*	2774	—	Flammable liquid	3	1 or 2
Phthalimide derivative pesticides, liquid, flammable, harmful, nos, *flash point less than 21°C*	2774	—	Flammable liquid	3	1 or 2
Phthalimide derivative pesticides, liquid, toxic, flammable, nos *flash point less than 21°C*	3007	—	Toxic substance	6.1	1 or 2
Phthalimide derivative pesticides, liquid, flammable, harmful, nos *flash point not less than 21°C*	3007	—	Flammable liquid	3	3
Phthalimide derivative pesticides, liquid, toxic, nos	3008	—	Toxic substance	6.1	1 or 2
Phthalimide derivative pesticides, liquid, harmful, nos	3008	—	Harmful substance	6.1	3

Name of Substance 1	Substance Identification No. 2	Emergency Action Code 3	Classification for Conveyance 4	UN Class 5	Packing Group 6
Phthalimide derivative pesticides, solid, toxic, nos	2773	—	Toxic substance	6.1	1 or 2
Phthalimide derivative pesticides, solid, harmful, nos	2773	—	Harmful substance	6.1	3
Potassium, metal alloys	1420	—	Substance which in contact with water emits flammable gas	4.3	2
Pyrophoric metals, nos *or* Pyrophoric alloys, nos	1383	—	Spontaneously combustible substance	4.2	2
Rare gases, mixtures	1979	—	Non-flammable compressed gas	2	—
Rare gases and nitrogen mixtures	1981	—	Non-flammable compressed gas	2	—
Rare gases and oxygen mixtures	1980	—	Non-flammable compressed gas	2	—
Refrigerant gases, nos	1078	—	Non-flammable compressed gas	2	—
Resin solution, flammable	1866	—	Flammable liquid	3	*
Rodenticides, nos	1681	—	Toxic substance	6.1	1 or 2

* Check with consignor

LIST OF DANGEROUS SUBSTANCES (Alphabetical)

PART 3 GROUPS OF SUBSTANCES NOT LISTED IN PARTS 1 AND 2

Name of Substance 1	Substance Identification No. 2	Emergency Action Code 3	Classification for Conveyance 4	UN Class 5	Packing Group 6
Rodenticides, nos	1681	—	Harmful substance	6.1	3
Substances which in contact with water emit flammable gas, nos	2813	—	Substance which in contact with water emits flammable gas	4.3	*
Substituted nitrophenol pesticides, liquid, flammable, toxic, nos, *flash point less than 21°C*	2780	—	Flammable liquid	3	1 or 2
Substituted nitrophenol pesticides, liquid, flammable, harmful, nos, *flash point less than 21°C*	2780	—	Flammable liquid	3	1 or 2
Substituted nitrophenol pesticides, liquid, toxic, flammable, nos, *flash point less than 21°C*	3013	—	Toxic substance	6.1	1 or 2
Substituted nitrophenol, pesticides, liquid, flammable, harmful, nos, *flash point not less than 21°C*	3013	—	Flammable liquid	3	3
Substituted nitrophenol pesticides, liquid, toxic, nos	3014	—	Toxic substance	6.1	1 or 2

* Check with consignor

Name of Substance 1	Substance Identification No. 2	Emergency Action Code 3	Classification for Conveyance 4	UN Class 5	Packing Group 6
Substituted nitrophenol pesticides, liquid, harmful, nos	3014	—	Harmful substance	6.1	3
Substituted nitrophenol pesticides, solid, toxic, nos	2779	—	Toxic substance	6.1	1 or 2
Substituted nitrophenol pesticides, solid, harmful, nos	2779	—	Harmful substance	6.1	3
Tars, liquid, *including road asphalt and oils, bitumen and cut-backs*	1999	—	Flammable liquid	3	*
Tear gas substances, nos, liquid *or* solid	1693	—	Toxic substance	6.1	2
Thallium compounds, nos	1707	—	Toxic substance	6.1	1 or 2
Thallium compounds, nos	1707	—	Harmful substance	6.1	3
Toxic liquids, corrosive, nos	2927	—	Toxic substance	6.1	1 or 2
Toxic liquids flammable, nos	2929	—	Toxic substance	6.1	1 or 2
Toxic liquids, nos	2810	—	Toxic substance	6.1	1 or 2
Toxic solids, corrosive, nos	2928	—	Toxic substance	6.1	1 or 2
Toxic solids, flammable, nos	2930	—	Toxic substance	6.1	1 or 2
Toxic solids, nos	2811	—	Toxic substance	6.1	1 or 2

* Check with consignor

Name	UN No.		Class		Packing group
Triazine pesticides, liquid, flammable, toxic nos *flash point less than 21°C*	2764	—	Flammable liquid	3	1 or 2
Triazine pesticides, liquid, flammable, harmful, nos *flash point less than 21°C*	2764	—	Flammable liquid	3	1 or 2
Triazine pesticides, liquid, toxic, flammable, nos, *flash point not less than 21°C*	2997	—	Toxic substance	6.1	1 or 2
Triazine pesticides, liquid, flammable harmful, nos, *flash point not less than 21°C*	2997	—	Flammable liquid	3	3
Trizine pesticides, liquid, toxic, nos	2998	—	Toxic substance	6.1	1 or 2
Triazine pesticides, liquid, harmful, nos	2998	—	Harmful substance	6.1	3
Triazine pesticides, liquid, toxic, nos	2763	—	Toxic substance	6.1	1 or 2
Triazine pesticides, solid, harmful, nos	2763	—	Harmful substance	6.1	3

* Check with Consignor.